edexcel

advancing learning, changing lives

BTEC National
Health and Social Care

Study Guide

A PEARSON COMPANY

BTEC National Study Guide: Health and Social Care

Published by:
Edexcel Limited
One90 High Holborn
London WC1V 7BH
www.edexcel.org.uk

Distributed by:
Pearson Education Limited
Edinburgh Gate
Harlow
Essex CM20 2JE

First published 2007
Fifth impression 2009

ISBN 978-1-84690-218-5

Project managed and typeset by Hart McLeod, Cambridge
Printed in Great Britain by Ashford Colour Press Ltd, Gosport, Hants.

Cover image © Lee Frost/Robert Harding Picture Library Ltd/Alamy

The publisher's policy is to use paper manufactured from sustainable forests.

All reasonable efforts have been made to trace and contact original copyright owners.

This material offers high quality support for the delivery of Edexcel qualifications.
This does not mean that it is essential to achieve any Edexcel qualification, nor does it mean that this is the only suitable material available to support any Edexcel qualification. No Edexcel-published material will be used verbatim in setting any Edexcel assessment and any resource lists produced by Edexcel shall include this and other appropriate texts.

Acknowledgements

p.42 ©Jose Luis Pelaez, Inc./Blend Images/Corbis; p.68 ©M Stock/Alamy; p.78 ©Jack Hollingsworth/Photodisc/Getty Images; p.105 t ©Image Source/Corbis, b ©Rob Barker; p.111 ©Comstock Select/Corbis; p.112 ©Bloomimage/Corbis; p.115 l ©Vikki Martin/Alamy, c ©Beenelux/zefa/Corbis, r ©DK. Khattiya/Alamy; p.125 ©Bill Brooks/Alamy; p.126 ©Terry Farmer/Stock Connection Distribution/Alamy

Contents

If you've already followed a BTEC First programme, you will know that this is an exciting way to study; if you are fresh from GCSEs you will find that from now on you will be in charge of your own learning. This guide has been written specially for you, to help get you started and then succeed on your BTEC National course.

The **Introduction** concentrates on making sure you have all the right facts about your course at your fingertips. Also, it guides you through the important skills you need to develop if you want to do well including:

■ managing your time

■ researching information

■ preparing a presentation.

Keep this by your side throughout your course and dip into it whenever you need to.

The **Activities** give you tasks to do on your own, in a small group or as a class. They will help you internalise your learning and then prepare for assessment by practising your skills and showing you how much you know. These activities are not for assessment.

The sample **Marked Assignments** show you what other students have done to gain Pass, Merit or Distinction. By seeing what past students have done, you should be able to improve your own grade.

Your BTEC National will cover six, twelve or eighteen units depending on whether you are doing an Award, Certificate or Diploma. In this guide the activities cover sections from Unit 1 – Developing Effective Communication in Health and Social Care, Unit 3 – Health, Safety and Security in Health and Social Care, Unit 4 – Development through the Life Stages and Unit 5 – Fundamentals of Anatomy and Physiology for Health and Social Care. These units underpin your study of Health and Social Care.

Because the guide covers only four units, it is essential that you do all the other work your tutors set you. You will have to research information in textbooks, in the library and on the Internet. You should have the opportunity to visit local organisations and welcome visiting speakers to your institution. This is a great way to find out more about your chosen vocational area – the type of jobs that are available and what the work is really like.

This guide is a taster, an introduction to your BTEC National. Use it as such and make the most of the rich learning environment that your tutors will provide for you. Your BTEC National will give you an excellent base for further study, a broad understanding of health and social care and the knowledge you need to succeed in the world of work. Remember, thousands of students have achieved a BTEC National and are now studying for a degree or at work, building a successful career.

INTRODUCTION

SEVEN STEPS TO SUCCESS ON YOUR BTEC NATIONAL

You have received this guide because you have decided to do a BTEC National qualification. You may even have started your course. At this stage you should feel good about your decision. BTEC Nationals have many benefits – they are well-known and respected qualifications, they provide excellent preparation for future work or help you to get into university if that is your aim. If you are already at work then gaining a BTEC National will increase your value to your employer and help to prepare you for promotion.

Despite all these benefits though, you may be rather apprehensive about your ability to cope. Or you may be wildly enthusiastic about the whole course! More probably, you are somewhere between the two – perhaps quietly confident most of the time but sometimes worried that you may get out of your depth as the course progresses. You may be certain you made the right choice or still have days when your decision worries you. You may understand exactly what the course entails and what you have to do – or still feel rather bewildered, given all the new stuff you have to get your head around.

Your tutors will use the induction sessions at the start of your course to explain the important information they want you to know. At the time, though, it can be difficult to remember everything. This is especially true if you have just left school and are now studying in a new environment, among a group of people you have only just met. It is often only later that you think of useful questions to ask. Sometimes, misunderstandings or difficulties may only surface weeks or months into a course – and may continue for some time unless they are quickly resolved.

This student guide has been written to help to minimise these difficulties, so that you get the most out of your BTEC National course from day one. You can read through it at your own pace. You can look back at it whenever you have a problem or query.

This Introduction concentrates on making sure you have all the right facts about your course at your fingertips. This includes a **Glossary** (on page 32) which explains the specialist terms you may hear or read – including words and phrases highlighted in bold type in this Introduction.

The Introduction also guides you through the important skills you need to develop if you want to do well – such as managing your time, researching information and preparing a presentation; as well as reminding you about the key skills you will need to do justice to your work, such as good written and verbal communications.

Make sure you have all the right facts

- Use the PlusPoint boxes in each section to help you to stay focused on the essentials.

- Use the Action Point boxes to check out things you need to know or do right now.

- Refer to the Glossary (on page 32) if you need to check the meaning of any of the specialist terms you may hear or read.

Remember, thousands of students have achieved BTEC National Diplomas and are now studying for a degree or at work, building a successful career. Many were nervous and unsure of themselves at the outset – and very few experienced absolutely no setbacks during the course. What they did have, though, was a belief in their own ability to do well if they concentrated on getting things right one step at a time. This Introduction enables you to do exactly the same!

STEP ONE

UNDERSTAND YOUR COURSE AND HOW IT WORKS

What is a BTEC qualification and what does it involve? What will you be expected to do on the course? What can you do afterwards? How does this National differ from 'A' levels or a BTEC First qualification?

All these are common questions – but not all prospective students ask them! Did you? And, if so, did you really listen to the answers? And can you remember them now?

If you have already completed a BTEC First course then you may know some of the answers – although you may not appreciate some of the differences between that course and your new one.

Let's start by checking out the basics.

- All BTEC National qualifications are **vocational** or **work-related**. This doesn't mean that they give you all the skills that you need to do a job. It does mean that you gain the specific knowledge and understanding relevant to your chosen subject or area of work. This means that when you start in a job you will learn how to do the work more quickly and should progress further. If you are already employed, it means you become more valuable to your employer. You can choose to study a BTEC National in a wide range of vocational areas, such as Business, Health and Social Care, IT, Performing Arts and many others.

- There are three types of BTEC National qualification and each has a different number of units.

    - The BTEC National Award usually has 6 units and takes 360 **guided learning hours (GLH)** to complete. It is often offered as a part-time or short course but you may be one of the many students doing an Award alongside A-levels as a full-time course. An Award is equivalent to one 'A' level.

    - The BTEC National Certificate usually has 12 units and takes 720 GLH to complete. You may be able to study for the Certificate on a part-time or full-time course. It is equivalent to two 'A' levels.

- The BTEC National Diploma usually has 18 units and takes 1080 GLH to complete. It is normally offered as a two-year full-time course. It is equivalent to three 'A' levels.

These qualifications are often described as **nested**. This means that they fit inside each other (rather like Russian dolls!) because the same units are common to them all. This means that if you want to progress from one to another you can do so easily by simply completing more units.

■ Every BTEC National qualification has a set number of **core units**. These are the compulsory units every student must complete. The number of core units you will do on your course depends upon the vocational area you are studying.

■ All BTEC National qualifications also have a range of **specialist units** from which you may be able to make a choice. These enable you to study particular areas in more depth.

■ Some BTEC National qualifications have **specialist core units**. These are mandatory units you will have to complete if you want to follow a particular pathway in certain vocational areas. Engineering is an example of a qualification with the overarching title, Engineering, which has a set of core units that all students must complete. Then, depending what type of engineering a student wants to follow, there are more specialist core units that must be studied.

■ On all BTEC courses you are expected to be in charge of your own learning. If you have completed a BTEC First, you will already have been introduced to this idea, but you can expect the situation to be rather different now that you are working at BTEC National level. Students on a BTEC First course will be expected to need more guidance whilst they develop their skills and find their feet. In some cases, this might last quite some time. On a BTEC National course you will be expected to take more responsibility for yourself and your own learning almost from the outset. You will quickly be expected to start thinking for yourself. This means planning what to do and carrying out a task without needing constant reminders. This doesn't mean that your tutor won't give you help and guidance when you need it. It does mean, though, that you need to be 'self-starting' and to be able to use your own initiative. You also need to be able to assess your own performance and make improvements when necessary. If you enjoy having the freedom to make your own decisions and work at your own pace then you will welcome this type of learning with open arms. However, there are dangers! If you are a procrastinator (look up this word if you don't know what it means!) then it's quite likely you will quickly get in a muddle. In this case read Step 3 – Use your time wisely – very carefully indeed!

■ The way you are assessed and graded on a BTEC course is different from an 'A' level course, although you will still obtain UCAS points which you need if you want to go to university. You can read about this in the next section.

PLUSPOINTS

+ You can usually choose to study part-time or full-time for your BTEC National and do an Award, Certificate or Diploma and progress easily from one to the other.

+ You will study both core units and specialist units on your course.

+ When you have completed your BTEC course you can get a job (or **apprenticeship**), use your qualification to develop your career and/or continue your studies to degree level.

+ You are responsible for your own learning on a BTEC course. This prepares you for life at work or at university when you will be expected to be self-starting and to use your own initiative.

ACTION POINTS

✓ Check you know whether you are studying for an Award, Certificate or Diploma and find out the number of units you will be studying for your BTEC National qualification.

✓ Find out which are core and which are specialist units, and which specialist units are offered at your school or college.

✓ Check out the length of your course and when you will be studying each unit.

✓ Explore the Edexcel website at www.edexcel.org.uk. Your first task is to find what's available for your particular BTEC National qualification. Start by finding National qualifications, then look for your vocational area and check you are looking at the 2007 schemes. Then find the specification for your course. Don't print this out – it is far too long. You could, of course, save it if you want to refer to it regularly or you could just look through it for interest and then bookmark the pages relating to your qualification for future reference.

✓ Score yourself out of 5 (where 0 is awful and 5 is excellent) on each of the following to see how much improvement is needed for you to become responsible for your own learning!

Being punctual; organisational ability; tidiness; working accurately; finding and correcting own mistakes; solving problems; accepting responsibility; working with details; planning how to do a job; using own initiative; thinking up new ideas; meeting deadlines.

✓ Draw up your own action plan to improve any areas where you are weak. Talk this through at your next individual **tutorial**.

STEP TWO

UNDERSTAND HOW YOU ARE ASSESSED AND GRADED – AND USE THIS KNOWLEDGE TO YOUR ADVANTAGE!

If you already have a BTEC First qualification, you may think that you don't need to read this section because you assume that BTEC National is simply more of the same. Whilst there are some broad similarities, you will now be working at an entirely different level and the grades you get for your work could be absolutely crucial to your future plans.

Equally, if you have opted for BTEC National rather than 'A' level because you thought you would have less work (or writing) to do then you need to read this section very carefully. Indeed, if you chose your BTEC National because you thought it would guarantee you an easy life, you are likely to get quite a shock when reality hits home!

It is true that, unlike 'A' levels, there are no exams on a BTEC course. However, to do well you need to understand the importance of your assignments, how these are graded and how these convert into unit points and UCAS points. This is the focus of this section.

Your assignments

On a BTEC National course your learning is assessed by means of **assignments** set by your tutors and given to you to complete throughout your course.

■ Your tutors will use a variety of **assessment methods**, such as case studies, projects, presentations and shows to obtain evidence of your skills and knowledge to date. You may also be given work-based or **time-constrained** assignments – where your performance might be observed and assessed. It will depend very much on the vocational area you are studying (see also page 16).

- Important skills you will need to learn are how to research information (see page 25) and how to use your time effectively, particularly if you have to cope with several assignments at the same time (see page 12). You may also be expected to work cooperatively as a member of a team to complete some parts of your assignments – especially if you are doing a subject like Performing Arts – or to prepare a presentation (see page 26).

- All your assignments are based on **learning outcomes** set by Edexcel. These are listed for each unit in your course specification. You have to meet *all* the learning outcomes to pass the unit.

Your grades

On a BTEC National course, assignments that meet the learning outcomes are graded as Pass, Merit or Distinction.

- The difference between these grades has very little to do with how much you write! Edexcel sets out the **grading criteria** for the different grades in a **grading grid**. This identifies the **higher-level skills** you have to demonstrate to earn a higher grade. You can find out more about this, and read examples of good (and not so good) answers to assignments at Pass, Merit and Distinction level in the marked assignments section starting on page 109. You will also find out more about getting the best grade you can in Step 5 – Understand your assessment – on page 16.

- Your grades for all your assignments earn you **unit points**. The number of points you get for each unit is added together and your total score determines your final grade(s) for the qualification – again either Pass, Merit or Distinction. You get one final grade if you are taking a BTEC National Award, two if you are taking a BTEC National Certificate and three if you are taking a BTEC National Diploma.

- Your points and overall grade(s) also convert to **UCAS points** which you will need if you want to apply to study on a degree course. As an example, if you are studying a BTEC National Diploma, and achieve three final pass grades you will achieve 120 UCAS points. If you achieve three final distinction grades the number of UCAS points you have earned goes up to 360.

- It is important to note that you start earning both unit and UCAS points from the very first assignment you complete! This means that if you take a long time to settle into your course, or to start working productively, you could easily lose valuable points for quite some time. If you have your heart set on a particular university or degree course then this could limit your choices. Whichever way you look at it, it is silly to squander potentially good grades for an assignment and their equivalent points, just because you didn't really understand what you had to do – which is why this guide has been written to help you!

■ If you take a little time to understand how **grade boundaries** work, you can see where you need to concentrate your efforts to get the best final grade possible. Let's give a simple example. Chris and Shaheeda both want to go to university and have worked hard on their BTEC National Diploma course. Chris ends with a total score of 226 unit points which converts to 280 UCAS points. Shaheeda ends with a total score of 228 unit points – just two points more – which converts to 320 UCAS points! This is because a score of between 204 and 227 unit points gives 280 UCAS points, whereas a score of 228 – 251 points gives 320 UCAS points. Shaheeda is pleased because this increases her chances of getting a place on the degree course she wants. Chris is annoyed. He says if he had known then he would have put more effort into his last assignment to get two points more.

■ It is always tempting to spend time on work you like doing, rather than work you don't – but this can be a mistake if you have already done the best you can at an assignment and it would already earn a very good grade. Instead you should now concentrate on improving an assignment which covers an area where you know you are weak, because this will boost your overall grade(s). You will learn more about this in Step 3 – use your time wisely.

PLUSPOINTS

+ Your learning is assessed in a variety of ways, such as by assignments, projects and case studies. You will need to be able to research effectively, manage your own time and work well with other people to succeed.

+ You need to demonstrate specific knowledge and skills to achieve the learning outcomes set by Edexcel. You need to demonstrate you can meet all the learning outcomes to pass a unit.

+ Higher-level skills are required for higher grades. The grading criteria for Pass, Merit and Distinction grades are set out in a grading grid for the unit.

+ The assessment grades of Pass, Merit and Distinction convert to unit points. The total number of unit points you receive during the course determines your final overall grade(s) and the UCAS points you have earned.

+ Working effectively from the beginning maximises your chances of achieving a good qualification grade. Understanding grade boundaries enables you to get the best final grade(s) possible.

ACTION POINTS

✓ Find the learning outcomes for the units you are currently studying. Your tutor may have given you these already, or you can find them in the specification for your course that you already accessed at www.edexcel.org.uk.

✓ Look at the grading grid for the units and identify the way the evidence required changes to achieve the higher grades. Don't worry if there are some words that you do not understand – these are explained in more detail on page 32 of this guide.

✓ If you are still unsure how the unit points system works, ask your tutor to explain it to you.

✓ Check out the number of UCAS points you would need for any course or university in which you are interested.

✓ Keep a record of the unit points you earn throughout your course and check regularly how this is affecting your overall grade(s), based on the grade boundaries for your qualification. Your tutor will give you this information or you can check it yourself in the specification for your course on the Edexcel website.

STEP THREE

USE YOUR TIME WISELY

Most students on a BTEC National course are trying to combine their course commitments with a number of others – such as a job (either full or part-time) and family responsibilities. In addition, they still want time to meet with friends, enjoy a social life and keep up hobbies and interests that they have.

Starting the course doesn't mean that you have to hide away for months if you want to do well. It does mean that you have to use your time wisely if you want to do well, stay sane and keep a balance in your life.

You will only do this if you make time work for you, rather than against you, by taking control. This means that you decide what you are doing, when you are doing it and work purposefully; rather than simply reacting to problems or panicking madly because you've yet another deadline staring you in the face.

This becomes even more important as your course progresses because your workload is likely to increase, particularly towards the end of a term. In the early days you may be beautifully organised and able to cope easily. Then you may find you have several tasks to complete simultaneously as well as some research to start. Then you get two assignments in the same week from different tutors – as well as having a presentation to prepare. Then another assignment is scheduled for the following week – and so on. This is not because your tutors are being deliberately difficult. Indeed, most will try to schedule your assignments to avoid such clashes. The problem, of course, is that none of your tutors can assess your abilities until you have learned something – so if several units start and end at the same time it is highly likely there will be some overlap between your assignments.

To cope when the going gets tough, without collapsing into an exhausted heap, you need to learn a few time management skills.

Use your time wisely

■ **Pinpoint where your time goes at the moment** Time is like money – it's usually difficult to work out where it all went! Work out how much time you currently spend at college, at work, at home and on social activities. Check, too, how much time you waste each week – and why this happens. Are you disorganised or do you easily get distracted? Then identify commitments that are vital and those that are optional so that you know where you can find time if you need to.

■ **Plan when and where to work** It is unrealistic not to expect to do quite a lot of work for your course in your own time. It is also better to work regularly, and in relatively short bursts, than to work just once or twice a week for very long stretches. In addition to deciding when to work, and for how long, you also need to think about when and where to work. If you are a lark, you will work better early in the day; if you are an owl, you will be at your best later on. Whatever time you work, you need somewhere quiet so that you can concentrate and with space for books and other resources you need. If the words 'quiet oasis' and 'your house' are totally incompatible at any time of the day or night

11

then check out the opening hours of your local and college library so that you have an escape route if you need it. If you are trying to combine studying with parental responsibilities it is sensible to factor in your children's commitments – and work around their bedtimes too! Store up favours, too, from friends and grandparents that you can call in if you get desperate for extra time when an assignment deadline is looming.

■ **Schedule your commitments** Keep a diary or (even better) a wall chart and write down every appointment you make or task you are given. It is useful to use a colour code to differentiate between personal and work or course commitments. You may also want to enter assignment review dates with your tutor in one colour and final deadline dates in another. Keep your diary or chart up-to-date by adding any new dates promptly every time you receive another task or assignment or whenever you make any other arrangements. Keep checking ahead so that you always have prior warning when important dates are looming. This stops you from planning a heavy social week when you will be at your busiest at work or college and from arranging a dental appointment on the morning when you and your team are scheduled to give an important presentation!

■ **Prioritise your work** This means doing the most important and urgent task first, rather than the one you like the most! Normally this will be the task or assignment with the nearest deadline. There are two exceptions. Sometimes you may need to send off for information and allow time for it to arrive. It is therefore sensible to do this first so that you are not held up later. The second is when you have to take account of other people's schedules – because you are working in a team or are arranging to interview someone, for example. In this case you will have to arrange your schedule around their needs, not just your own.

■ **Set sensible timescales** Trying to do work at the last minute or in a rush is never satisfactory, so it is wise always to allocate more time than you think you will need, never less. Remember, too, to include all the stages of a complex task or assignment, such as researching the information, deciding what to use, creating a first draft, checking it and making improvements and printing it out. If you are planning to do any of your work in a central facility always allow extra time and try to start work early. If you arrive at the last minute you may find every computer and printer is fully utilised until closing time.

■ **Learn self-discipline!** This means not putting things off (procrastinating!) because you don't know where to start or don't feel in the mood. Unless you are ill, you have to find some way of persuading yourself to work. One way is to bribe yourself. Make a start and promise yourself that if you work productively for 30 minutes then you deserve a small reward. After 30 minutes you may have become more engrossed and want to keep going a little longer. Otherwise at least you have made a start, so it's easier to come back and do more later. It doesn't matter whether you have research to do, an assignment to write up, a coaching session to plan, or lines to learn, you need to be self-disciplined.

■ **Take regular breaks and keep your life in balance** Don't go to the opposite extreme and work for hours on end. Take regular breaks to give yourself a rest and a change of activity. You need to recharge your batteries! Similarly, don't cancel every social arrangement so that you can work 24/7. Whilst this may be occasionally necessary if you have several deadlines looming simultaneously, it should only be a last resort. If you find yourself doing this regularly then go back to the beginning of this section and see where your time–management planning is going wrong.

PLUSPOINTS

+ Being in control of your time enables you to balance your commitments according to their importance and allows you not let to anyone down – including yourself.

+ Controlling time involves knowing how you spend (and waste!) your time now, planning when best to do work, scheduling your commitments and setting sensible timescales for work to be done.

+ Knowing how to prioritise means that you will schedule work effectively according to its urgency and importance but this also requires self-discipline. You have to follow the schedule you have set for yourself!

+ Managing time and focusing on the task at hand means you will do better work and be less stressed, because you are not having to react to problems or crises. You can also find the time to include regular breaks and leisure activities in your schedule.

ACTION POINTS

✓ Find out how many assignments you can expect to receive this term and when you can expect to receive these. Enter this information into your student diary or onto a planner you can refer to regularly.

✓ Update your diary and/or planner with other commitments that you have this term – both work/college-related and social. Identify any potential clashes and decide the best action to take to solve the problem.

✓ Identify your own best time and place to work quietly and effectively.

✓ Displacement activities are things we do to put off starting a job we don't want to do – such as sending texts, watching TV, checking emails etc. Identify yours so that you know when you're doing them!

STEP FOUR

UTILISE ALL YOUR RESOURCES

Your resources are all the things that can help you to achieve your qualification. They can therefore be as wide-ranging as your favourite website and your **study buddy** (see below) who collects handouts for you if you miss a class.

Your college will provide the essential resources for your course, such as a library with a wide range of books and electronic reference sources, learning resource centre(s), the computer network and Internet access. Other basic resources you will be expected to provide yourself, such as file folders and paper. The policy on textbooks varies from one college to another, but on most courses today students are expected to buy their own. If you look after yours carefully, then you have the option to sell it on to someone else afterwards and recoup some of your money. If you scribble all over it, leave it on the floor and then tread on it, turn back pages and rapidly turn it into a dog-eared, misshapen version of its former self then you miss out on this opportunity.

13

Unfortunately students often squander other opportunities to utilise resources in the best way – usually because they don't think about them very much, if at all. To help, below is a list of the resources you should consider important – with a few tips on how to get the best out of them.

- **Course information** This includes your course specification, this Study Guide and all the other information relating to your BTEC National which you can find on the Edexcel website. Add to this all the information given to you at college relating to your course, including term dates, assignment dates and, of course, your timetable. This should not be 'dead' information that you glance at once and then discard or ignore. Rather it is important reference material that you need to store somewhere obvious, so that you can look at it whenever you have a query or need to clarify something quickly.

- **Course materials** In this group is your textbook (if there is one), the handouts you are given as well as print-outs and notes you make yourself. File handouts the moment you are given them and put them into an A4 folder bought for the purpose. You will need one for each unit you study. Some students prefer lever-arch files but these are more bulky so more difficult to carry around all day. Unless you have a locker at college it can be easier to keep a lever arch file at home for permanent storage of past handouts and notes for a unit and carry an A4 folder with you which contains current topic information. Filing handouts and print-outs promptly means they don't get lost. They are also less likely to get crumpled, torn or tatty becoming virtually unreadable. Unless you have a private and extensive source of income then this is even more important if you have to pay for every print-out you take in your college resource centre. If you are following a course such as Art and Design, then there will be all your art materials and the pieces you produce. You must look after these with great care.

- **Other stationery items** Having your own pens, pencils, notepad, punch, stapler and sets of dividers is essential. Nothing irritates tutors more than watching one punch circulate around a group – except, perhaps, the student who trudges into class with nothing to write on or with. Your dividers should be clearly labelled to help you store and find notes, print-outs and handouts fast. Similarly, your notes should be clearly headed and dated. If you are writing notes up from your own research then you will have to include your source. Researching information is explained in Step 6 – Sharpen your skills.

- **Equipment and facilities** These include your college library and resource centres, the college computer network and other college equipment you can use, such as laptop computers, photocopiers and presentation equipment. Much of this may be freely available; others – such as using the photocopier in the college library or the printers in a resource centre – may cost you money. Many useful resources will be electronic, such as DVDs or electronic journals and databases. At home you may have your own computer with Internet access to count as a resource. Finally, include any specialist equipment and facilities available for your particular course that you use at college or have at home.

Utilise all your resources

All centralised college resources and facilities are invaluable if you know how to use them – but can be baffling when you don't. Your induction should have included how to use the library, resource centre(s) and computer network. You should also have been informed of the policy on using IT equipment which determines what you can and can't do when you are using college computers. If, by any chance, you missed this then go and check it out for yourself. Library and resource centre staff will be only too pleased to give you helpful advice – especially if you pick a quiet time to call in. You can also find out about the allowable ways to transfer data between your college computer and your home computer if your options are limited because of IT security.

Having a study buddy is a good idea

- **People** You are surrounded by people who are valuable resources: your tutor(s), specialist staff at college, your employer and work colleagues, your relatives and any friends who have particular skills or who work in the same area you are studying. Other members of your class are also useful resources – although they may not always seem like it! Use them, for example, to discuss topics out of class time. A good debate between a group of students can often raise and clarify issues that there may not be time to discuss fully in class. Having a study buddy is another good idea – you get/make notes for them when they are away and vice versa. That way you don't miss anything.

If you want information or help from someone, especially anyone outside your immediate circle, then remember to get the basics right! Approach them courteously, do your homework first so that you are well-prepared and remember that you are asking for assistance – not trying to get them to do the work for you! If someone has agreed to allow you to interview them as part of your research for an assignment or project then good preparations will be vital, as you will see in Step 6 – Sharpen your Skills (see page 22).

One word of warning: be wary about using information from friends or relatives who have done a similar or earlier course. First, the slant of the material they were given may be different. It may also be out-of-date. And *never* copy anyone else's written assignments. This is **plagiarism** – a deadly sin in the educational world. You can read more about this in Step 5 – Understand your assessment (see page 16).

- **You!** You have the ability to be your own best resource or your own worst enemy! The difference depends upon your work skills, your personal skills and your attitude to your course and other people. You have already seen how to use time wisely. Throughout this guide you will find out how to sharpen and improve other work and personal skills and how to get the most out of your course – but it is up to you to read it and apply your new-found knowledge! This is why attributes like a positive attitude, an enquiring mind and the ability to focus on what is important all have a major impact on your final result.

15

PLUSPOINTS

+ Resources help you to achieve your qualification. You will squander these unwittingly if you don't know what they are or how to use them properly.

+ Course information needs to be stored safely for future reference: course materials need to be filed promptly and accurately so that you can find them quickly.

+ You need your own set of key stationery items; you also need to know how to use any central facilities or resources such as the library, learning resource centres and your computer network.

+ People are often a key resource – school or college staff, work colleagues, members of your class, people who are experts in their field.

+ You can be your own best resource! Develop the skills you need to be able to work quickly and accurately and to get the most out of other people who can help you.

ACTION POINTS

✓ Under the same headings as in this section, list all the resources you need for your course and tick off those you currently have. Then decide how and when you can obtain anything vital that you lack.

✓ Check that you know how to access and use all the shared resources to which you have access at school or college.

✓ Pair up with someone on your course as a study buddy – and don't let them down!

✓ Test your own storage systems. How fast can you find notes or print-outs you made yesterday/last week/last month – and what condition are they in?

✓ Find out the IT policy at your school or college and make sure you abide by it.

STEP FIVE

UNDERSTAND YOUR ASSESSMENT

The key to doing really, really well on any BTEC National course is to understand exactly what you are expected to do in your assignments – and then to do it! It really is as simple as that. So why is it that some people go wrong?

Obviously you may worry that an assignment may be so difficult that it is beyond you. Actually this is highly unlikely to happen because all your assignments are based on topics you will have already covered thoroughly in class. Therefore, if you have attended regularly – and have clarified any queries or worries you have either in class or during your tutorials – this shouldn't happen. If you have had an unavoidable lengthy absence then you may need to review your progress with your tutor and decide how best to cope with the situation. Otherwise, you should note that the main problems with assignments are usually due to far more mundane pitfalls – such as:

✗ not reading the instructions or the assignment brief properly

✗ not understanding what you are supposed to do

✗ only doing part of the task or answering part of a question

✗ skimping the preparation, the research or the whole thing

✗ not communicating your ideas clearly

✗ guessing answers rather than researching properly

✗ padding out answers with irrelevant information

✗ leaving the work until the last minute and then doing it in a rush

✗ ignoring advice and feedback your tutor has given you.

You can avoid all of these traps by following the guidelines below so that you know exactly what you are doing, prepare well and produce your best work.

The assignment 'brief'

The word 'brief' is just another way of saying 'instructions'. Often, though, a 'brief' (despite its name!) may be rather longer. The brief sets the context for the work, defines what evidence you will need to produce and matches the grading criteria to the tasks. It will also give you a schedule for completing the tasks. For example, a brief may include details of a case study you have to read; research you have to carry out or a task you have to do, as well as questions you have to answer. Or it may give you details about a project or group presentation you have to prepare. The type of assignments you receive will depend partly upon the vocational area you are studying, but you can expect some to be in the form of written assignments. Others are likely to be more practical or project-based, especially if you are doing a very practical subject such as Art and Design, Performing Arts or Sport. You may also be assessed in the workplace. For example, this is a course requirement if you are studying Children's Care, Learning and Development.

The assignment brief may also include the **learning outcomes** to which it relates. These tell you the purpose of the assessment and the knowledge you need to demonstrate to obtain a required grade. If your brief doesn't list the learning outcomes, then you should check this information against the unit specification to see the exact knowledge you need to demonstrate.

The grade(s) you can obtain will also be stated on the assignment brief. Sometimes an assignment will focus on just one grade. Others may give you the opportunity to develop or extend your work to progress to a higher grade. This is often dependent upon submitting acceptable work at the previous grade first. You will see examples of this in the Marked Assignment section of this Study Guide on page 109.

The brief will also tell you if you have to do part of the work as a member of a group. In this case, you must identify your own contribution. You may also be expected to take part in a **peer review**, where you all give feedback on the contribution of one another. Remember that you should do this as objectively and professionally as possible – not just praise everyone madly in the hope that they will do the same for you! In any assignment where there is a group contribution, there is virtually always an individual component, so that your individual grade can be assessed accurately.

Finally, your assignment brief should state the final deadline for handing in the work as well as any interim review dates when you can discuss your progress and ideas with your tutor. These are very important dates indeed and should be entered immediately into your diary or planner. You should schedule your work around these dates so that you have made a start by the first date. This will then enable you to note any queries or significant issues you want to discuss. Otherwise you will waste a valuable opportunity to obtain useful feedback on your progress. Remember, too, to take a notebook to any review meetings so that you can write down the guidance you are given.

Your school or college rules and regulations

Your school or college will have a number of policies and guidelines about assignments and assessment. These will deal with issues such as:

■ The procedure you must follow if you have a serious personal problem so cannot meet the deadline date and need an extension.

■ Any penalties for missing a deadline date without any good reason.

■ The penalties for copying someone else's work (**plagiarism**). These will be severe so make sure that you never share your work (including your CDs) with anyone else and don't ask to borrow theirs.

■ The procedure to follow if you are unhappy with the final grade you receive.

Even though it is unlikely that you will ever need to use any of these policies, it is sensible to know they exist, and what they say, just as a safeguard.

Understanding the question or task

There are two aspects to a question or task that need attention. The first are the *command words*, which are explained below. The second are the *presentation instructions*, so that if you are asked to produce a table or graph or report then you do exactly that – and don't write a list or an essay instead!

Command words are used to specify how a question must be answered, eg 'explain', 'describe', 'analyse', 'evaluate'. These words relate to the type of answer required. So whereas you may be asked to 'describe' something at Pass level, you will need to do more (such as 'analyse' or 'evaluate') to achieve Merit or Distinction grade.

Many students fail to get a higher grade because they do not realise the difference between these words. They simply don't know *how* to analyse or evaluate, so give an explanation instead. Just adding to a list or giving a few more details will never give you a higher grade – instead you need to change your whole approach to the answer.

The **grading grid** for each unit of your course gives you the command words, so that you can find out exactly what you have to do in each unit, to obtain a Pass, Merit and Distinction. The following charts show you what is usually required when you see a particular command word. You can use this, and the marked assignments on pages 109–160, to see the difference between the types of answers required for each grade. (The assignments your centre gives you will be specially written to ensure you have the opportunity to achieve all the possible grades.) Remember, though, that these are just examples to guide you. The exact response will often depend upon the way a question is worded, so if you have any doubts at all check with your tutor before you start work.

There are two other important points to note:

- Sometimes the same command word may be repeated for different grades – such as 'create' or 'explain'. In this case the *complexity* or *range* of the task itself increases at the higher grades – as you will see if you read the grading grid for the unit.
- Command words can also vary depending upon your vocational area. If you are studying Performing Arts or Art and Design you will probably find several command words that an Engineer or IT Practitioner would not – and vice versa!

To obtain a Pass grade

To achieve this grade you must usually demonstrate that you understand the important facts relating to a topic and can state these clearly and concisely.

Command word	What this means
Create (or produce)	Make, invent or construct an item.
Describe	Give a clear, straightforward description that includes all the main points and links these together logically.
Define	Clearly explain what a particular term means and give an example, if appropriate, to show what you mean.
Explain . . . how/why	Set out in detail the meaning of something, with reasons. It is often helpful to give an example of what you mean. Start with the topic then give the 'how' or 'why'.
Identify	Distinguish and state the main features or basic facts relating to a topic.
Interpret	Define or explain the meaning of something.
Illustrate	Give examples to show what you mean.
List	Provide the information required in a list rather than in continuous writing.
Outline	Write a clear description that includes all the main points but avoid going into too much detail.
Plan (or devise)	Work out and explain how you would carry out a task or activity.
Select (and present) information	Identify relevant information to support the argument you are making and communicate this in an appropriate way.
State	Write a clear and full account.
Undertake	Carry out a specific activity.
Examples: **Identify** the main features on a digital camera. **Describe** your usual lifestyle. **Outline** the steps to take to carry out research for an assignment.	

19

To obtain a Merit grade

To obtain this grade you must prove that you can apply your knowledge in a specific way.

Command word	What this means
Analyse	Identify separate factors, say how they are related and how each one relates to the topic.
Classify	Sort your information into appropriate categories before presenting or explaining it.
Compare and contrast	Identify the main factors that apply in two or more situations and explain the similarities and differences or advantages and disadvantages.
Demonstrate	Provide several relevant examples or appropriate evidence which support the arguments you are making. In some vocational areas this may also mean giving a practical performance.
Discuss	Provide a thoughtful and logical argument to support the case you are making.
Explain (in detail)	Provide details and give reasons and/or evidence to clearly support the argument you are making.
Implement	Put into practice or operation. You may also have to interpret or justify the effect or result.
Interpret	Understand and explain an effect or result.
Justify	Give appropriate reasons to support your opinion or views and show how you arrived at these conclusions.
Relate/report	Give a full account of, with reasons.
Research	Carry out a full investigation.
Specify	Provide full details and descriptions of selected items or activities.

Examples:
Compare and contrast the performance of two different digital cameras.
Justify your usual lifestyle.
Explain in detail the steps to take to research an assignment.

To obtain a Distinction grade

To obtain this grade you must prove that you can make a reasoned judgement based on appropriate evidence.

Command word	What this means
Analyse	Identify the key factors, show how they are linked and explain the importance and relevance of each.
Assess	Give careful consideration to all the factors or events that apply and identify which are the most important and relevant with reasons for your views.
Comprehensively explain	Give a very detailed explanation that covers all the relevant points and give reasons for your views or actions.
Comment critically	Give your view after you have considered all the evidence, particularly the importance of both the relevant positive and negative aspects.
Evaluate	Review the information and then bring it together to form a conclusion. Give evidence to support each of your views or statements.
Evaluate critically	Review the information to decide the degree to which something is true, important or valuable. Then assess possible alternatives taking into account their strengths and weaknesses if they were applied instead. Then give a precise and detailed account to explain your opinion.
Summarise	Identify and review the main, relevant factors and/or arguments so that these are explained in a clear and concise manner.

Examples:

Assess ten features commonly found on a digital camera.

Evaluate critically your usual lifestyle.

Analyse your own ability to carry out effective research for an assignment.

Responding positively

This is often the most important attribute of all! If you believe that assignments give you the opportunity to demonstrate what you know and how you can apply it *and* positively respond to the challenge by being determined to give it your best shot, then you will do far better than someone who is defeated before they start.

It obviously helps, too, if you are well organised and have confidence in your own abilities – which is what the next section is all about!

PLUSPOINTS

+ Many mistakes in assignments are through errors that can easily be avoided such as not reading the instructions properly or doing only part of the task that was set!

+ Always read the assignment brief very carefully indeed. Check that you understand exactly what you have to do and the learning outcomes you must demonstrate.

+ Make a note of the deadline for an assignment and any interim review dates on your planner. Schedule work around these dates so that you can make the most of reviews with your tutor.

+ Make sure you know about school or college policies relating to assessment, such as how to obtain an extension or query a final grade.

+ For every assignment, make sure you understand the command words, which tell you how to answer the question, and the presentation instructions, which say what you must produce.

+ Command words are shown in the grading grid for each unit of your qualification. Expect command words and/or the complexity of a task to be different at higher grades, because you have to demonstrate higher-level skills.

ACTION POINTS

✓ Discuss with your tutor the format (style) of assignments you are likely to receive on your course, eg assignments, projects, or practical work where you are observed.

✓ Check the format of the assignments in the Marked Assignments section of this book. Look at the type of work students did to gain a Pass and then look at the difference in the Merit answers. Read the tutor's comments carefully and ask your own tutor if there is anything you do not understand.

✓ Check out all the policies and guidelines at your school or college that relate to assessment and make sure you understand them.

✓ Check out the grading grid for the units you are currently studying and identify the command words for each grade. Then check you understand what they mean using the explanations above. If there are any words that are not included, ask your tutor to explain the meanings and what you would be required to do.

STEP SIX

SHARPEN YOUR SKILLS

To do your best in any assignment you need a number of skills. Some of these may be vocationally specific, or professional, skills that you are learning as part of your course – such as acting or dancing if you are taking a Performing Arts course or, perhaps, football if you are following a Sports course. Others, though, are broader skills that will help you to do well in assignments no matter what subjects or topics you are studying – such as communicating clearly and cooperating with others.

Some of these skills you will have already and in some areas you may be extremely proficient. Knowing where your weaknesses lie, though, and doing something about them has many benefits. You will work more quickly, more accurately *and* have increased confidence in your own abilities. As an extra bonus, all these skills also make you more effective at work – so there really is no excuse for not giving yourself a quick skills check and then remedying any problem areas.

This section contains hints and tips to help you check out and improve each of the following areas:

- Your numeracy skills
- Keyboarding and document preparation
- Your IT skills
- Your written communication skills
- Working with others
- Researching information
- Making a presentation

Your numeracy skills

Some people have the idea that they can ignore numeracy because this skill isn't relevant to their vocational area – such as Art and Design or Children's Care, Learning and Development. If this is how you think then you are wrong! Numeracy is a life skill that everyone needs, so if you can't carry out basic calculations accurately then you will have problems, often when you least expect them.

Fortunately there are several things you can do to remedy this situation:

- Practise basic calculations in your head and then check them on a calculator.
- Ask your tutor if there are any essential calculations which give you difficulties.
- Use your onscreen calculator (or a spreadsheet package) to do calculations for you when you are using your computer.
- Try your hand at Sudoku puzzles – either on paper or by using a software package or online at sites such as www.websudoku.com/.
- Investigate puzzle sites and brain training software, such as http://school.discovery.com/brainboosters/ and Dr Kawashima's Brain Training by Nintendo.
- Check out online sites such as www.bbc.co.uk/skillswise/ and www.bbc.co.uk/schools/ks3bitesize/maths/number/index.shtml to improve your skills.

Numeracy is a life skill

Keyboarding and document preparation

- Think seriously about learning to touch type to save hours of time! Your school or college may have a workshop you can join or you can learn online such as by downloading a free program at www.sense-lang.org/typing/ or practising on sites such as www.computerlab.kids.new.net/keyboarding.htm.
- Obtain correct examples of document formats you will have to use, such as a report or summary. Your tutor may provide you with these or you can find examples in many communication textbooks.
- Proofread work you produce on a computer *carefully*. Remember that your spell checker will not pick up every mistake you make, such as a mistyped word that makes another word (eg form/from; sheer/shear)

23

and grammar checkers, too, are not without their problems! This means you still have to read your work through yourself. If possible, let your work go 'cold' before you do this so that you read it afresh and don't make assumptions about what you have written. Then read word by word to make sure it still makes sense and there are no silly mistakes, such as missing or duplicated words.

- Make sure your work looks professional by using an appropriate typeface and font size as well as suitable margins.
- Print out your work carefully and store it neatly, so it looks in pristine condition when you hand it in.

Your IT skills

- Check that you can use the main features of all the software packages that you will need to produce your assignments, such as Word, Excel and PowerPoint.
- Adopt a good search engine, such as Google, and learn to use it properly. Many have online tutorials such as www.googleguide.com.
- Develop your IT skills to enable you to enhance your assignments appropriately. For example, this may include learning how to import and export text and artwork from one package to another; taking digital photographs and inserting them into your work and/or creating drawings or diagrams by using appropriate software for your course.

Your written communication skills

A poor vocabulary will reduce your ability to explain yourself clearly; work peppered with spelling or punctuation errors looks unprofessional.

- Read more. This introduces you to new words and familiarises you over and over again with the correct way to spell words.
- Look up words you don't understand in a dictionary and then try to use them yourself in conversation.
- Use the Thesaurus in Word to find alternatives to words you find yourself regularly repeating, to add variety to your work.
- *Never* use words you don't understand in the hope that they sound impressive!
- Do crosswords to improve your word power and spelling.
- Resolve to master punctuation – especially apostrophes – either by using an online programme or working your way through the relevant section of a communication textbook that you like.
- Check out online sites such as www.bbc.co.uk/skillswise/ and www.bbc.co.uk/schools/gcsebitesize/english/ as well as puzzle sites with communication questions such as http://school.discovery.com/brainboosters/.

Working with others

In your private life you can choose who you want to be with and how you respond to them. At work you cannot do that – you are paid to be professional and this means working alongside a wide variety of people, some of whom you may like and some of whom you may not!

The same applies at school or college. By the time you have reached BTEC National level you will be expected to have outgrown wanting to work with your best friends on every project! You may not be very keen on everyone who is in the same team as you, but – at the very least – you can be pleasant, cooperative and helpful. In a large group this isn't normally too difficult. You may find it much harder if you have to partner someone who has very different ideas and ways of working to you.

In this case it may help if you:

- Realise that everyone is different and that your ways of working may not always be the best!
- Are prepared to listen and contribute to a discussion (positively) in equal amounts. Make sure, too, that you encourage the quiet members of the group to speak up by asking them what their views are. The ability to draw other people into the discussion is an important and valuable skill to learn.
- Write down what you have said you will do, so that you don't forget anything.
- Are prepared to do your fair share of the work.
- Discuss options and alternatives with people – don't give them orders or meekly accept instructions and then resent it afterwards.
- Don't expect other people to do what you wouldn't be prepared to do.
- Are sensitive to other people's feelings and remember that they may have personal problems or issues that affect their behaviour.
- *Always* keep your promises and never let anyone down when they are depending upon you.
- Don't flounce around or lose your temper if things get tough. Instead take a break while you cool down. Then sit down and discuss the issues that are annoying you.
- Help other people to reach a compromise when necessary, by acting as peacemaker.

Researching information

Poor researchers either cannot find what they want or find too much – and then drown in a pile of papers. If you find yourself drifting aimlessly around a library when you want information or printing out dozens of pages for no apparent purpose, then this section is for you!

- Always check *exactly* what it is you need to find and how much detail is needed. Write down a few key words to keep yourself focused.
- Discipline yourself to ignore anything that is irrelevant – from books with interesting titles to websites which sound tempting but have little to do with your topic or key words.
- Remember that you could theoretically research information forever! So at some time you have to call a halt. Learning when to do this is another skill, but you can learn this by writing out a schedule which clearly states when you have to stop looking and start sorting out your information and writing about it!

- In a library, check you know how the books are stored and what other types of media are available. If you can't find what you are looking for then ask the librarian for help. Checking the index in a book is the quickest way to find out whether it contains information related to your key words. Put it back if it doesn't or if you can't understand it. If you find three or four books and/or journals that contain what you need then that is usually enough.

- Online use a good search engine and use the summary of the search results to check out the best sites. Force yourself to check out sites beyond page one of the search results! When you enter a site investigate it carefully – use the site map if necessary. It isn't always easy to find exactly what you want. Bookmark sites you find helpful and will want to use again and only take print-outs when the information is closely related to your key words.

- Talk to people who can help you (see also Step 4 – Utilise all your resources) and prepare in advance by thinking about the best questions to ask. Always explain why you want the information and don't expect anyone to tell you anything that is confidential or sensitive – such as personal information or financial details. Always write clear notes so that you remember what you have been told, by whom and when. If you are wise you will also note down their contact details so that you can contact them again if you think of anything later. If you remember to be courteous and thank them for their help, this shouldn't be a problem.

- Store all your precious information carefully and neatly in a labelled folder so that you can find it easily. Then, when you are ready to start work, reread it and extract that which is most closely related to your key words and the task you are doing.

- Make sure you state the source of all the information you quote by including the name of the author or the web address, either in the text or as part of a bibliography at the end. Your school or college will have a help sheet which will tell you exactly how to do this.

Making a presentation

This involves several skills – which is why it is such a popular way of finding out what students can do! It will test your ability to work in a team, speak in public and use IT (normally PowerPoint) – as well as your nerves. It is therefore excellent practice for many of the tasks you will have to do when you are at work – from attending an interview to talking to an important client.

You will be less nervous if you have prepared well and have rehearsed your role beforehand. You will produce a better, more professional presentation if you take note of the following points.

- If you are working as a team, work out everyone's strengths and weaknesses and divide up the work (fairly) taking these into account. Work out, too, how long each person should speak and who would be the best as the 'leader' who introduces each person and then summarises everything at the end.

PLUSPOINTS

+ Poor numeracy skills can let you down in your assignments and at work. Work at improving these if you regularly struggle with even simple calculations.

+ Good keyboarding, document production and IT skills can save you hours of time and mean that your work is of a far more professional standard. Improve any of these areas which are letting you down.

+ Your written communication skills will be tested in many assignments. Work at improving areas of weakness, such as spelling, punctuation or vocabulary.

+ You will be expected to work cooperatively with other people both at work and during many assignments. Be sensitive to other people's feelings, not just your own, and always be prepared to do your fair share of the work and help other people when you can.

+ To research effectively you need to know exactly what you are trying to find and where to look. This means understanding how reference media is stored in your library as well as how to search online. Good organisation skills also help so that you store important information carefully and can find it later. And never forget to include your sources in a bibliography.

+ Making a presentation requires several skills and may be nerve-racking at first. You will reduce your problems if you prepare well, are not too ambitious and have several run-throughs beforehand. Remember to speak clearly and a little more slowly than normal and smile from time to time!

ACTION POINTS

✓ Test both your numeracy and literacy skills at http://www.move-on.org.uk/testyourskills.asp# to check your current level. You don't need to register on the site if you click to do the 'mini-test' instead. If either need improvement, get help at http://www.bbc.co.uk/keyskills/it/1.shtml.

✓ Do the following two tasks with a partner to jerk your brain into action!

  – Each write down 36 simple calculations in a list, eg 8 x 6, 19 – 8, 14 + 6. Then exchange lists. See who can answer the most correctly in the shortest time.

  – Each write down 30 short random words (no more than 8 letters), eg cave, table, happily. Exchange lists. You each have three minutes to try to remember as many words as possible. Then hand back the list and write down all those you can recall. See who can remember the most.

✓ Assess your own keyboarding, proof-reading, document production, written communication and IT skills. Then find out if your tutors agree with you!

✓ List ten traits in other people that drive you mad. Then, for each one, suggest what you could do to cope with the problem (or solve it) rather than make a fuss. Compare your ideas with other members of your group.

✓ Take a note of all feedback you receive from your tutors, especially in relation to working with other people, researching and giving presentations. In each case focus on their suggestions and ideas so that you continually improve your skills throughout the course.

■ Don't be over-ambitious. Take account of your time-scale, resources and the skills of the team. Remember that a simple, clear presentation is often more professional than an over-elaborate or complicated one where half the visual aids don't work properly!

■ If you are using PowerPoint try to avoid preparing every slide with bullet points! For variety, include some artwork and vary the designs. Remember that you should *never* just read your slides to the audience! Instead prepare notes that you can print out that will enable you to enhance and extend what the audience is reading.

- Your preparations should also include checking the venue and time; deciding what to wear and getting it ready; preparing, checking and printing any handouts; deciding what questions might be asked and how to answer these.

- Have several run-throughs beforehand and check your timings. Check, too, that you can be heard clearly. This means lifting up your head and 'speaking' to the back of the room a little more slowly and loudly than you normally do.

- On the day, arrive in plenty of time so that you aren't rushed or stressed. Remember that taking deep breaths helps to calm your nerves.

- Start by introducing yourself clearly and smile at the audience. If it helps, find a friendly face and pretend you are just talking to that person.

- Answer any questions honestly and don't exaggerate, guess or waffle. If you don't know the answer then say so!

- If you are giving the presentation in a team, help out someone else who is struggling with a question if you know the answer.

- Don't get annoyed or upset if you get any negative feedback afterwards. Instead take note so that you can concentrate on improving your own performance next time. And don't focus on one or two criticisms and ignore all the praise you received! Building on the good and minimising the bad is how everyone improves in life!

STEP SEVEN

MAXIMISE YOUR OPPORTUNITIES AND MANAGE YOUR PROBLEMS

Like most things in life, you may have a few ups and downs on your course – particularly if you are studying over quite a long time, such as one or two years. Sometimes everything will be marvellous – you are enjoying all the units, you are up-to-date with your work, you are finding the subjects interesting and having no problems with any of your research tasks. At other times you may struggle a little more. You may find one or two topics rather tedious, or there may be distractions or worries in your personal life that you have to cope with. You may struggle to concentrate on the work and do your best.

Rather than just suffering in silence or gritting your teeth if things go a bit awry it is sensible if you have an action plan to help you cope. Equally, rather than just accepting good opportunities for additional experiences or learning, it is also wise to plan how to make the best of these. This section will show you how to do this.

Making the most of your opportunities

The following are examples of opportunities to find out more about information relevant to your course or to try putting some of your skills into practice.

- **External visits** You may go out of college on visits to different places or organisations. These are not days off – there is a reason for making each trip. Prepare in advance by reading around relevant topics and make notes of useful information whilst you are there. Then write (or type) it up neatly as soon as you can and file it where you can find it again!

- **Visiting speakers** Again, people are asked to talk to your group for a purpose. You are likely to be asked to contribute towards questions that may be asked – which may be submitted in advance so that the speaker is clear on the topics you are studying. Think carefully about information that you would find helpful so that you can ask one or two relevant and useful questions. Take notes whilst the speaker is addressing your group, unless someone is recording the session. Be prepared to thank the speaker on behalf of your group if you are asked to do so.

- **Professional contacts** These will be the people you meet on work experience doing the real job that one day you hope to do. Make the most of meeting these people to find out about the vocational area of your choice.

- **Work experience** If you need to undertake practical work for any particular units of your BTEC National qualification, and if you are studying full-time, then your tutor will organise a work experience placement for you and talk to you about the evidence you need to obtain. You may also be issued with a special log book or diary in which to record your experiences. Before you start your placement, check that you are clear about all the details, such as the time you will start and leave, the name of your supervisor, what you should wear and what you should do if you are ill during the placement and cannot attend. Read and reread the units to which your evidence will apply and make sure you understand the grading criteria and what you need to obtain. Then make a note of appropriate headings to record your information. Try to make time to write up your notes, log book and/or diary every night, whilst your experiences are fresh in your mind.

- **In your own workplace** You may be studying your BTEC National qualification on a part-time basis and also have a full-time job in the same vocational area. Or you may be studying full-time and have a part-time job just to earn some money. In either case you should be alert to opportunities to find out more about topics that relate to your workplace, no matter how generally. For example, many BTEC courses include topics such as health and safety, teamwork, dealing with customers, IT security and communications – to name but a few. All these are topics that your employer will have had to address and finding out more about these will broaden your knowledge and help to give more depth to your assignment responses.

- **Television programmes, newspapers, Podcasts and other information sources** No matter what vocational area you are studying, the media are likely to be an invaluable source of information. You should be alert to any news bulletins that relate to your studies as well as relevant information in more topical television programmes. For example, if you are studying Art and Design then you should make a particular effort to watch the *Culture Show* as well as programmes on artists, exhibitions or other topics of interest. Business students should find inspiration by watching *Dragons Den*, *The Apprentice* and the *Money Programme* and Travel and Tourism students should watch holiday, travel and adventure programmes. If you are studying Media, Music and Performing Arts then you are spoiled for choice! Whatever your vocational choice, there will be television and radio programmes of special interest to you.

Remember that you can record television programmes to watch later if you prefer, and check out newspaper headlines online and from sites such as BBC news. The same applies to Podcasts. Of course, to know which information is relevant means that you must be familiar with the content of all the units you are studying, so it is useful to know what topics you will be learning about in the months to come, as well as the ones you are covering now. That way you can recognise useful opportunities when they arise.

Minimising problems

If you are fortunate, any problems you experience on your course will only be minor ones. For example, you may struggle to keep yourself motivated every single day and there may be times that you are having difficulty with a topic. Or you may be struggling to work with someone else in your team or to understand a particular tutor.

The media are invaluable sources of information

During induction you should have been told which tutor to talk to in this situation, and who to see if that person is absent or if you would prefer to see someone else. If you are having difficulties which are distracting you and affecting your work then it is sensible to ask to see your tutor promptly so that you can talk in confidence, rather than just trusting to luck everything will go right again. It is a rare student who is madly enthusiastic about every part of a course and all the other people on the course, so your tutor won't be surprised and will be able to give you useful guidance to help you stay on track.

If you are very unlucky, you may have a more serious personal problem to deal with. In this case it is important that you know the main sources of help in your school or college and how to access these.

- **Professional counselling** There may be a professional counselling service if you have a concern that you don't want to discuss with any teaching staff. If you book an appointment to see a counsellor then you can be certain that nothing you say will ever be mentioned to another member of staff without your permission.

- **Student complaint procedures** If you have a serious complaint to make then the first step is to talk to a tutor, but you should be aware of the formal student complaint procedures that exist if you cannot resolve the problem informally. Note that these are only used for serious issues, not for minor difficulties.

- **Student appeals procedures** If you cannot agree with a tutor about a final grade for an assignment then you need to check the grading criteria and ask the tutor to explain how the grade was awarded. If you are still unhappy then you should see your personal tutor. If you still disagree then you have the right to make a formal appeal.

- **Student disciplinary procedures** These exist so that all students who flout the rules in a school or college will be dealt with in the same way. Obviously it is wise to avoid getting into trouble at any time, but if you find yourself on the wrong side of the regulations do read the procedures carefully to see what could happen. Remember that being honest about what happened and making a swift apology is always the wisest course of action, rather than being devious or trying to blame someone else.

■ **Serious illness** Whether this affects you or a close family member, it could severely affect your attendance. The sooner you discuss the problem with your tutor the better. This is because you will be missing notes and information from the first day you do not attend. Many students under-estimate the ability of their tutors to find inventive solutions in this type of situation – from sending notes by post to updating you electronically if you are well enough to cope with the work.

PLUSPOINTS	ACTION POINTS
+ Some students miss out on opportunities to learn more about relevant topics. This may be because they haven't read the unit specifications, so don't know what topics they will be learning about in future; haven't prepared in advance or don't take advantage of occasions when they can listen to an expert and perhaps ask questions. Examples of these occasions include external visits, visiting speakers, work experience, being at work and watching television.	✓ List the type of opportunities available on your course for obtaining more information and talking to experts. Then check with your tutor to make sure you haven't missed out any.
+ Many students encounter minor difficulties, especially if their course lasts a year or two. It is important to talk to your tutor, or another appropriate person, promptly if you have a worry that is affecting your work.	✓ Check out the content of each unit you will be studying so that you know the main topics you have still to study.
	✓ Identify the type of information you can find on television, in newspapers and in Podcasts that will be relevant to your studies.
+ All schools and colleges have procedures for dealing with important issues and problems such as serious complaints, major illnesses, student appeals and disciplinary matters. It is important to know what these are.	✓ Check out your school or college documents and procedures to make sure that you know who to talk to in a crisis and who you can see if the first person is absent.
	✓ Find out where you can read a copy of the main procedures in your school or college that might affect you if you have a serious problem. Then do so.

AND FINALLY . . .

Don't expect this Introduction to be of much use if you skim through it quickly and then put it to one side. Instead, refer to it whenever you need to remind yourself about something related to your course.

The same applies to the rest of this Student Guide. The Activities in the next section have been written to help you to demonstrate your understanding of many of the key topics contained in the core or specialist units you are studying. Your tutor may tell you to do these at certain times; otherwise there is nothing to stop you working through them yourself!

Similarly, the Marked Assignments in the final section have been written to show you how your assignments may be worded. You can also see the type of response that will achieve a Pass, Merit and Distinction – as well as the type of response that won't! Read these carefully and if any comment or grade puzzles you, ask your tutor to explain it.

Then keep this guide in a safe place so that you can use it whenever you need to refresh your memory. That way, you will get the very best out of your course – and yourself!

GLOSSARY

Note: all words highlighted in bold in the text are defined in the glossary.

Accreditation of Prior Learning (APL)

APL is an assessment process that enables your previous achievements and experiences to count towards your qualification providing your evidence is authentic, current, relevant and sufficient.

Apprenticeships

Schemes that enable you to work and earn money at the same time as you gain further qualifications (an **NVQ** award and a technical certificate) and improve your key skills. Apprentices learn work-based skills relevant to their job role and their chosen industry. You can find out more at www.apprenticeships.org.uk/

Assessment methods

Methods, such as **assignments**, case studies and practical tasks, used to check that your work demonstrates the learning and understanding required for your qualification.

Assessor

The tutor who marks or assesses your work.

Assignment

A complex task or mini-project set to meet specific **grading criteria**.

Awarding body

The organisation which is responsible for devising, assessing and issuing qualifications. The awarding body for all BTEC qualifications is Edexcel.

Core units

On a BTEC National course these are the compulsory or mandatory units that all students must complete to gain the qualification. Some BTEC qualifications have an over-arching title, eg Engineering, but within Engineering you can choose different routes. In this case you will study both common core units that are common to all engineering qualifications and **specialist core unit(s)** which are specific to your chosen **pathway**.

Degrees

These are higher education qualifications which are offered by universities and colleges. Foundation degrees take two years to complete; honours degrees may take three years or longer. See also **Higher National Certificates and Diplomas**.

DfES

The Department for Education and Skills: this is the government department responsible for education issues. You can find out more at www.dfes.gov.uk

Distance learning

This enables you to learn and/or study for a qualification without attending an Edexcel centre although you would normally be supported by a member of staff who works there. You communicate with your tutor and/or the centre that organises the distance learning programme by post, telephone or electronically.

Educational Maintenance Award (EMA)

This is a means-tested award which provides eligible students under 19, who are studying a full-time course at school or college, with a cash sum of money every week. See http://www.dfes.gov.uk/financialhelp/ema/ for up-to-date details.

External verification

Formal checking by a representative of Edexcel of the way a BTEC course is delivered. This includes sampling various assessments to check content and grading.

Final major project

This is a major, individual piece of work that is designed to enable you to demonstrate you have achieved several learning outcomes for a BTEC National qualification in the creative or performing arts. Like all assessments, this is internally assessed.

Forbidden combinations

Qualifications or units that cannot be taken simultaneously because their content is too similar.

GLH

See **Guided Learning Hours** below.

Grade

The rating (Pass, Merit or Distinction) given to the mark you have obtained which identifies the standard you have achieved.

Grade boundaries

The pre-set points at which the total points you have earned for different units converts to the overall grade(s) for your qualification.

Grading criteria

The standard you have to demonstrate to obtain a particular grade in the unit, in other words, what you have to prove you can do.

Grading domains

The main areas of learning which support the **learning outcomes**. On a BTEC National course these are: application of knowledge and understanding; development of practical and technical skills; personal development for occupational roles; application of generic and **key skills**. Generic skills are basic skills needed wherever you work, such as the ability to work cooperatively as a member of a team.

Grading grid

The table in each unit of your BTEC qualification specification that sets out the **grading criteria**.

Guided Learning Hours (GLH)

The approximate time taken to deliver a unit which includes the time taken for direct teaching, instruction and assessment and for you to carry out directed assignments or directed individual study. It does not include any time you spend on private study or researching an assignment. The GLH determines the size of the unit. At BTEC National level, units are either 30, 60, 90 or 120 guided learning hours. By looking at the number of GLH a unit takes, you can see the size of the unit and how long it is likely to take you to learn and understand the topics it contains.

Higher education (HE)

Post-secondary and post-further education, usually provided by universities and colleges.

Higher level skills

Skills such as evaluating or critically assessing complex information that are more difficult than lower level skills such as writing a description or making out a list. You must be able to demonstrate higher level skills to achieve a Distinction grade.

Higher National Certificates and Diplomas

Higher National Certificates and Diplomas are vocational qualifications offered at colleges around the country. Certificates are part-time and designed to be studied by people who are already in work; students can use their work experiences to build on their learning. Diplomas are full-time courses – although often students will spend a whole year on work experience part way through their Diploma. Higher Nationals are roughly equivalent to half a degree.

Indicative reading

Recommended books and journals whose content is both suitable and relevant for the unit.

Induction

A short programme of events at the start of a course designed to give you essential information and introduce you to your fellow students and tutors so that you can settle down as quickly and easily as possible.

Internal verification

The quality checks carried out by nominated tutor(s) at your school or college to ensure that all assignments are at the right level and cover appropriate learning outcomes. The checks also ensure that all **assessors** are marking work consistently and to the same standard.

Investors in People (IIP)

A national quality standard which sets a level of good practice for the training and development of people. Organisations must demonstrate their commitment to achieve the standard.

Key skills

The transferable, essential skills you need both at work and to run your own life successfully. They are: literacy, numeracy, IT, problem solving, working with others and self-management.

Learning and Skills Council (LSC)

The government body responsible for planning and funding education and training for everyone aged over 16 in England - except university students. You can find out more at www.lsc.gov.uk

Learning outcomes

The knowledge and skills you must demonstrate to show that you have effectively learned a unit.

Learning support

Additional help that is available to all students in a school or college who have learning difficulties or other special needs. These include reasonable adjustments to help to reduce the effect of a disability or difficulty that would place a student at a substantial disadvantage in an assessment situation.

Levels of study

The depth, breadth and complexity of knowledge, understanding and skills required to achieve a qualification determines its level. Level 2 is broadly equivalent to GCSE level (grades A*-C) and level 3 equates to GCE level. As you successfully achieve one level, you can then progress on to the next. BTEC qualifications are offered at Entry level, then levels 1, 2, 3, 4 and 5.

Local Education Authority (LEA)

The local government body responsible for providing education for students of compulsory school age in your area.

Mentor

A more experienced person who will guide and counsel you if you have a problem or difficulty.

Mode of delivery

The way in which a qualification is offered to students, eg part-time, full-time, as a short course or by **distance learning**.

National Occupational Standard (NOS)

These are statements of the skills, knowledge and understanding you need to develop to be competent at a particular job. These are drawn up by the **Sector Skills Councils**.

National Qualification Framework (NQF)

The framework into which all accredited qualifications in the UK are placed. Each is awarded a level based on their difficulty which ensures that all those at the same level are of the same standard. (See also **levels of study**).

National Vocational Qualification (NVQ)

Qualifications which concentrate upon the practical skills and knowledge required to do a job competently. They are usually assessed in the workplace and range from level 1 (the lowest) to level 5 (the highest).

Nested qualifications

Qualifications which have 'common' units, so that students can easily progress from one to another by adding on more units, such as the BTEC Award, BTEC Certificate and BTEC Diploma.

Pathway

All BTEC National qualifications are comprised of a small number of core units and a larger number of specialist units. These specialist units are grouped into different combinations to provide alternative pathways to achieving the qualification, linked to different career preferences.

Peer review

An occasion when you give feedback on the performance of other members in your team and they, in turn, comment on your performance.

Plagiarism

The practice of copying someone else's work and passing it off as your own. *This is strictly forbidden on all courses.*

Portfolio

A collection of work compiled by a student, usually as evidence of learning to produce for an **assessor**.

Professional body

An organisation that exists to promote or support a particular profession, such as the Law Society and the Royal Institute of British Architects.

Professional development and training

Activities that you can undertake, relevant to your job, that will increase and/or update your knowledge and skills.

Project

A comprehensive piece of work which normally involves original research and investigation either by an individual or a team. The findings and results may be presented in writing and summarised in a presentation.

Qualifications and Curriculum Authority (QCA)

The public body, sponsored by the **DfES**, responsible for maintaining and developing the national curriculum and associated assessments, tests and examinations. It also accredits and monitors qualifications in colleges and at work. You can find out more at www.qca.gov.uk

Quality assurance

In education, this is the process of continually checking that a course of study is meeting the specific requirements set down by the awarding body.

Sector Skills Councils (SSCs)

The 25 employer-led, independent organisations that are responsible for improving workforce skills in the UK by identifying skill gaps and improving learning in the workplace. Each council covers a different type of industry and develops its **National Occupational Standards**.

Semester

Many universities and colleges divide their academic year into two halves or semesters, one from September to January and one from February to July.

Seminar

A learning event between a group of students and a tutor. This may be student-led, following research into a topic which has been introduced earlier.

Specialist core units

See under **Core units**.

Study buddy

A person in your group or class who takes notes for you and keeps you informed of important developments if you are absent. You do the same in return.

Time-constrained assignment

An assessment you must complete within a fixed time limit.

Tutorial

An individual or small group meeting with your tutor at which you can discuss the work you are currently doing and other more general course issues. At an individual tutorial your progress on the course will be discussed and you can also raise any concerns or personal worries you have.

The University and Colleges Admissions Service (UCAS)

The central organisation which processes all applications for higher education courses. You pronounce this 'You-Cass'.

UCAS points

The number of points allocated by **UCAS** for the qualifications you have obtained. **HE** institutions specify how many points you need to be accepted on the courses they offer. You can find out more at www.ucas.com

Unit abstract

The summary at the start of each BTEC unit that tells you what the unit is about.

Unit content

Details about the topics covered by the unit and the knowledge and skills you need to complete it.

Unit points

The number of points you have gained when you complete a unit. These depend upon the grade you achieve (Pass, Merit or Distinction) and the size of the unit as determined by its **guided learning hours**.

Vocational qualification

A qualification which is designed to develop the specific knowledge and understanding relevant to a chosen area of work.

Work experience

Any time you spend on an employer's premises when you carry out work-based tasks as an employee but also learn about the enterprise and develop your skills and knowledge.

ACTIVITIES

This section focuses on: P1, P2, P3, P4, P5, P6, M1, M2, M3, D1, D2.

Introduction and learning outcomes

All health and social care professionals require good communication skills in order to carry out their roles effectively. It is, therefore, important for those embarking on a career in these sectors to gain knowledge and understanding of the skills involved in communication in order to develop and enhance their own ability.

1 Understand effective communication and interpersonal interaction.

2 Understand factors that influence communication and interpersonal interactions in health and social care settings.

3 Know how patients/service users may be assisted by effective communication.

4 Be able to demonstrate own communication skills in a caring role.

Content

1) Understanding effective communication and interpersonal interaction

Types of communication: eg one-to-one, groups, formal, informal, text, oral, visual, touch, music and drama, arts and crafts, communication using technology.

Types of interpersonal interaction: eg speech, language (eg first language, dialect, slang, jargon), non-verbal (eg posture, facial expression, touch, silence, proximity, reflective listening), variation between cultures, listening and reflecting back.

Communication cycle: ideas occur; message coded; message sent; message received; message decoded; message understood.

2) Understand factors that influence communication and interpersonal interactions in health and social care settings

Communication and language needs and preferences: the individual's preferred spoken language; the use of signs, symbols, pictures and writing; objects of reference; communication passports; human and technological aids to communication.

Environment: eg setting, noise, seating, lighting.

Behaviour: eg attitude, assertiveness, aggressiveness, submissiveness; responses to behaviour; effects on identity, self-esteem and self-image of others.

Barriers: eg type of communication (eg difficult, complex, sensitive), language needs/preferences,

disability, personality, environment, time, self-esteem, anxiety, depression, assumptions, cultural differences, value and belief systems, stereotypes, use and abuse of power.

In relation to the integrated workforce agenda: communication with professionals, multi-agency working, multi-professional working.

3) Know how patients/service users may be assisted by effective communication

Support services: advocates; interpreters; translators; signers; others eg speech therapists, counsellors, mentors, befrienders, psychologists.

Technology: aids and adaptations; text facility on mobile phones.

Preferred language: eg Makaton, signing, Braille, first language.

Supporting: empowerment; promotion of rights; maintaining confidentiality.

4) Be able to demonstrate own communication skills in a caring role

Communication skills: verbal; non-verbal.

Effectiveness: in supporting patients/service users.

Key people: eg relatives, friends, health and social care workers.

Grading criteria

P1 describe different types of communication and interpersonal interaction, using examples relevant to health and social care settings

To meet P1 you will describe both verbal and non-verbal communication (facial expressions, gestures etc); one to one and group communications with service users and key workers, also communication through music, drama, technology, arts and crafts etc. You should use examples from work placement to support your descriptions.

P2 describe the stages of the communication cycle

You will investigate precisely how communication works and why misunderstandings occur.

P3 describe factors that may influence communication and interpersonal interactions with particular reference to health and social care settings

Factors will include language needs and preferences as well as factors specific to health and social care settings, eg visual or aural difficulties etc.

P4 identify how the communication needs of patients/service users may be assisted, including non-verbal communication

You might be aware of the use of hearing aids, mobile phones and Braille, but you will also investigate how symbols, signs, Communication Passports etc. help service users.

P5 describe two interactions that they have participated in, in the role of a carer, using communication skills to assist patients/service users

Referring to work placement (or role-play) describe how you have used your communication skills effectively to help service users/patients.

P6 review the effectiveness of own communication skills in the two interactions undertaken

Go over the two interactions to see how well (or not!) they worked. You might find it useful to apply the communication cycle to your interactions.

M1 explain how the communication cycle may be used to communicate difficult, complex and sensitive issues

As a health or care worker you might find that you have to break sensitive news to a service user, a relative or friend; your understanding of how communication works will help you when tact, diplomacy and empathy are needed.

M2 explain the specific communication needs patients/service users may have that require support, including the use of technology

Communication needs will include language requirements, disabilities, emotional or psychological needs etc. You will also investigate the relevance of the environment to effective communication.

M3 explain how own communication skills could have been used to make the interactions more effective

Following your review of the two interactions, how could you improve your communication skills?

D1 analyse how communication in health and social care settings assists patients/service users and other key people

You will examine how service users and workers all benefit from effective communication, eg how and when should information about service users/patients be passed between key workers?

D2 analyse the factors that influenced the interactions undertaken

Use the chain of communication to help identify and evaluate the way in which the activity (interaction) took place.

UNDERSTAND EFFECTIVE COMMUNICATION AND INTERPERSONAL INTERACTION

ACTIVITY 1

Why do we communicate?

It could be said that the reasons for communicating can be broken down into three specific categories:

- To educate
- To inform
- To entertain

But in those three categories we can also include other reasons for communicating:

- To instruct
- To motivate
- To persuade
- To encourage
- To negotiate
- To understand

How do we communicate?

We all know about talking – and we use the sense of 'hearing' to listen.

We also use non-verbal communication (NVC) – and use the sense of 'sight' to watch people.

But what about the other senses, do we use any of the other senses to communicate? – Touch? Taste? Smell?

We use all of our five senses to communicate and receive information whether directly or indirectly.

Copy the chart below and complete columns 1 and 2 with examples of communication that use each of the senses:

Sense	Example 1	Example 2
Sight		
Sound		
Smell		
Taste		
Touch		

ACTIVITY 2

COMMUNICATION – EASY?

On a scale of one to ten (with one being very bad and ten being very good), how good do you think your skills of description are?

Work with a partner – but do not let your partner see what you are doing.

Draw a picture using all of the following shapes:

- Four horizontal lines
- Eight vertical lines
- Five circles
- Two squares
- A semicircle
- Three triangles
- Five rectangles

When you have finished your drawing, ask your partner to draw it as you describe it – you must not tell your partner how you have composed the picture or pattern that you have made, just describe it carefully!

When you have finished, compare the drawings – are they very different?

Why is that?

Now, on a scale of one to ten (with one being very bad and ten being very good), how good do you think you are at describing things? Are your description skills better or worse than you originally thought?

ACTIVITY 3

TYPES OF COMMUNICATION

Communication can be formal and informal; it can be written or spoken; it can take place between two people or many; and, as we have already seen, communication occurs for many reasons.

Consider the last time you were in a health or a care setting, describe the different types of communication that you might have seen – or have been involved in.

Examples

Type	Description
One-to-one	Doctor receiving and giving information

Communication – non-verbal

Professor Albert Mehrabian established this classic statistic for the effectiveness of spoken communications:

- 7% of meaning is in the words that are spoken
- 38% of meaning is paralinguistic (the way that the words are said)
- 55% of meaning is in facial expression

Professor Mehrabian used these statistics as the basis for his theory of the difference between words and meanings.

Understanding the difference between words and meaning is a vital capability for effective communications and relationships. For example, as John Ruskin put it:

'The essence of lying is in deception, not in words.' (John Ruskin, 1819–1900, English art critic and social commentator).

How can this theory be applied to the health and social care setting?

Example:

Carer: How are you today, Mrs Kaur?

Mrs Kaur: I'm fine, thank you.

From reading the words it might appear that Mrs Kaur has no problems.

If we could listen-in to the conversation then we might hear intonation in Mrs Kaur's voice that indicates that she is not as fine as she says.

If we could watch the conversation taking place then we might see that Mrs Kaur is sitting in a dejected manner, looking at the floor rather than at her carer.

ACTIVITY 4

ROLE-PLAY

Task 1

Work in small groups with one person acting as a carer and one person as a service user, the rest of the group should act as observers.

The carer and the service user should decide the direction the conversation should take – whether the carer is giving information or good news; the service user is feeling ill or angry etc.

Carry out an exchange putting a different interpretation on the conversation each time.

At the end of each exchange the observers should make notes that analyse how the tone and pitch, volume, emphasis, speed, pauses, facial expressions, gestures, eye contact, touch, proximity are all used when communicating emotions.

Task 2

As a class, compare the notes that have been made – how much use was made of non-verbal communication during the exchange?

Non-verbal communication can have one of four major uses:

1) to assist speech, eg by emphasising meaning

2) as a replacement for speech, eg using gestures such as raised eyebrows instead of asking a question

3) to signal attitude, eg trying to look unworried and cool by taking up a relaxed posture

4) signalling emotion, eg we can often tell if someone is happy or sad or angry by the way they might sit or stand.

If people are comfortable with each other and communicate well, they often copy each other's body language – this is called mirroring, but it is important to know the difference between mirroring and mimicking!

Task 3

For a week keep a 'body language' diary. Every time you are in a social area – a restaurant, a club etc – pay attention to the body language around you. Can you recognise those who are friends and those who have just fallen out? Make a note of the body language people use and what you think it means.

Communication – non-verbal

From the exercise you have just completed you should be able to identify the importance of non-verbal communication.

Non-verbal communication (NVC) plays an important part in the process of counselling when empathy and responsiveness can help to build up trust and can encourage openness.

However, is NVC as important as Professor Mehrabian's theory suggests?

ACTIVITY 5

Task 1

With a partner make a list of examples – related to health or social care settings – that DO NOT support the theory.

Task 2

As a class, discuss and devise a code of practice that will help ensure that when using any of these NVC methods for communicating, your message is received and understood.

eg   Does your sentence mean what you want it to?

Is your spelling accurate?

ACTIVITY 6

TECHNOLOGY

The prefix 'techno' relates to art, craft, practical or mechanical skills – not just to 'high tech' scientific applications.

Using this definition we could say that 'Technology' has been used as a means of communicating since time began:

- Cavemen painted on walls to tell stories or pass on information.
- North American Indians used smoke signals to send warnings.
- Beacons were lit to send messages many kilometres.
- Church bells, sirens are often set off to warn of danger or emergency.
- Flags (or arms) are still used to deliver information by semaphore.
- Emoticons.

Task 1

Using the above information as a starting point, research the history of one area of 'technological' communication.

Task 2

In a group of three or four, develop a poster that tells some of the story of communication.

ACTIVITY 7

COMMUNICATING – HOW IT'S DONE

Whatever the purpose of a communication, it is a two-way process that is not completed until the message has been received and understood – even if the understanding is not what was intended.

Problems with communication can occur at any point in the process:

Aiming --- Encoding --- Transmitting --- Receiving --- Decoding --- Responding

Look at this list of statements. To which of the six points does each statement belong?

STATEMENT	POINT OF PROCESS
What do you want to communicate?	
Is the information prioritised?	
What would make the receiver interested?	
Who are you communicating with?	
What is the best way to communicate this?	
What language should I use?	
What assumptions am I making about the receiver?	
What might the receiver assume about me that will influence the communication?	
Will there be any distractions that will make communication difficult?	
Can the receiver read/see/hear what you want to communicate?	
Is what you are communicating consistent with the way you're saying/writing/showing it?	
We think three times faster than we speak – it's easy for the speaker's words to get muddled with thoughts in our head.	
Ask for explanations.	
Ask for clarification – the responsibility of the message belongs to the sender, not the receiver.	
Ensure that no steps are missed out.	

ACTIVITY 8

CHAIN/CYCLE OF COMMUNICATION

Look at the Chain of Communication on the previous page and compare it with the communication cycle depicted on page 47 – both diagrams depict the same information.

Why do you think this?

Using examples from your work placement, present one of the diagrams to your colleagues demonstrating where communication can be misinterpreted and how misunderstandings can be corrected.

Stage	Process	Points to check
Aiming (ideas occur)	Decide what you want to say and choose the right words Understand the other person	Clarify your objectives What will the other person want from the message? What will be the emotional impact of the message?
Encoding (message encoded)	Choose the right method (phone call/group meeting etc) Sending the message Giving non-verbal signals	Make sure there are not more than approximately five ideas to transmit Is the language suitable? Are the words you say consistent with the non-verbal signals you give?
Transmitting (message sent)	Distractions? Deal with distortions	Avoid noise and interruptions Is the seating correct?
Receiving (message received)	Perceiving the message Listening actively	What phrases, facts and inferences are you looking for? Test your understanding of the message
Decoding (message decoded)	Make sense of the message Understand the other person	What do they mean? What is the 'hidden agenda'? How will you handle it if it does not fit in with your principles or beliefs?
Responding (message understood)	Encoding the message Starting the next message	To keep the communication going – agree, nod, smile To stop the communication – look bored, stop eye contact

A COMMUNICATION CYCLE

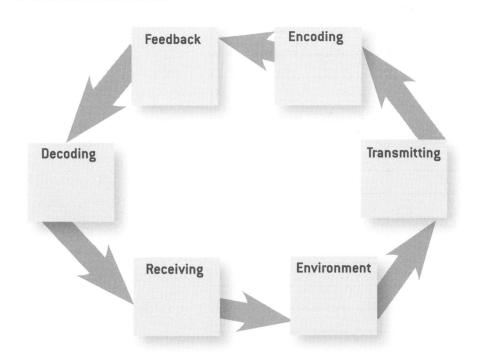

ACTIVITY 9

COMMUNICATION IN PRACTICE – ROLE-PLAY

Working in groups of three, one of you to be a care worker, the others to be an elderly couple. One of the couple is a disabled person who will be using a wheelchair for the first time.

The care worker is to explain to the couple how to use the wheelchair.

The couple must follow the directions precisely.

The care worker must give instructions which are followed precisely.

Relate the exercise to the communication cycle. Was the exercise successful? If not, at what point in the cycle did it go wrong?

ACTIVITY 10

COMMUNICATION CYCLE

Using your knowledge and understanding of the communication cycle put yourself in the position of the senior care worker on duty having to inform relatives that their 92 year old mother has accused a member of staff of theft. You might have to speak to them:

1) On the telephone

2) When they arrive at the care home

What points should you consider before you communicate with the relatives?

ACTIVITY 11

JARGON

Within the world of Health and Social Care, communication is often complicated by the use of jargon, acronyms and abbreviations.

Look at the list below – what do the terms really mean?

Abbreviation/ jargon/acronym	Could mean?	Actually means:
AIDS	Aid me! Help! Help!	
BP	Bed pan	
CABG	Cabbage	
DAT	Baby talk – dis and dat	
FPA	Feel pretty awful	
GP	Generally poor	
MMR	Mine, mine – really!	
NHS	Not healthy sis!	
NICE	Nice one guys!	
NKDA	Not known, didn't ask!	
NRT	No race track	
PALS	Pulling against library services	
SSD	Special services device	
STI	Silent team initiative	
WHO	A rock band from the 70s	

Remember this activity! Always think before you use jargon or abbreviations – does everyone know what you're talking about?

ACTIVITY 12

MUSIC AND DRAMA

Have you been to the theatre? Or have any theatrical companies come to your school to put on a production?

Task 1

- Discuss with a friend the information and feelings that you had at the end of the performance.
- Make notes that highlight the aim of the performance (was it giving a message or for entertainment?).
- Include your opinion on the value and the effectiveness of the performance.

Can you think of any advertisements, either on the television or at the cinema, that deliver a particular message?

Task 2

- With a colleague, list as many advertising messages as you can, then discuss the effectiveness of the message:

Was it easy to get the meaning?

Did you think that it was directed at the correct group of people?

Do you think the message would influence that group of people?

Why do you think that?

If the message was not influential, how would you change it to make it effective?

Task 3

Choose one advertisement that you both agree on – that was particularly good or particularly poor at communicating. Prepare a poster to present to the rest of the class identifying how or why the advertisement worked.

Music and drama are often used as a means of entertainment, but they can also be used to deliver messages.

Task 4

- **In small groups**, devise a role-play to deliver a health or care-related message.
- Decide which group of people your message is aimed at.
- Deliver your message to the rest of the class.
- Ask the class for feedback on the impact of the message – not on your acting abilities!
- Did they 'get the message'?

UNDERSTAND FACTORS THAT INFLUENCE COMMUNICATION AND INTERPERSONAL INTERACTIONS IN HEALTH AND SOCIAL CARE SETTINGS

ACTIVITY 13

NON-VERBAL COMMUNICATION

Non-verbal communication can be not only an effective means of transmitting a message, for some people it is the best way for them to communicate.

You are a support worker at the local hospital in either the audiology department or the eye clinic.

Task 1

Using a non-verbal means of communication, design a method of informing the patients/service users – some of whom might have learning difficulties – about a series of activities that will be happening over the next month at the local community centre.

Task 2

Design a questionnaire or survey for the rest of your class that will inform you of the success of your information-giving and advise you of improvements you could make.

Task 3

Present your information to the rest of the class – and then ask each member to complete the survey.

Task 4

Analyse the information gathered from the survey and write an evaluation of your skills of communicating with non-verbal information. Remember to say how you could have done the job better and what you will improve next time.

ACTIVITY 14

PHYSICAL BARRIERS

Over recent years many banks and building societies have removed the glass screen in front of the cashier to improve communication with customers. Perhaps the most important place for good interpersonal skills is in the field of health and social care, yet physical barriers are in place which hinder effective communication.

Task 1

Are you aware of any physical barriers in the health and social care sector that are being removed to help communicate with patients/service users? **As a class**, brainstorm your ideas for what makes physical barriers and what could constitute improvements.

Task 2

You are on a panel of advisers making recommendations for the upgrading and renovation of your local health centre. Write a short report that identifies areas where barriers to interpersonal interaction and communication occur and give your reasons why they should be removed.

ACTIVITY 15

TECHNOLOGICAL AIDS

Amongst all the recent 'hi-tech' aids, the computer must be one of the most important. Computers can be found in most, if not all, health and social care settings.

Task 1

In pairs, devise a list of people in the health and social care sector who might use a computer or a device containing a computer chip, giving as many reasons as you can for the use of computers/computer chips in the health and social care sector. Remember to include service users/patients and workers.

Task 2

Having made your list, consider the drawbacks of using computers/computer chips and write a paragraph on each.

Task 3

Select two drawbacks, then present your information to the rest of your class.

ACTIVITY 16

CONVERSATION

It is said that conversation is a dying art.

Do you think the above statement is true?

Write an article justifying your opinion and using examples from the health or social care sector.

You might wish to include the influence or otherwise of any of the following technologies:

- mobile phones, BlackBerrys, iPods
- emails
- blogging
- chat rooms
- soundbites
- chatshows
- synchronous and asynchronous conversation
- phone-in shows.

ACTIVITY 17

CSI-UK

This activity is in two parts, the instructions here are for all. Further instructions for the teacher/tutor are on p.53.

This activity is for the whole group. Some people should act as observers and timekeepers as well as participating.

Time-keepers will let the group know how long they have left.

Observers should study the ways people contribute or do not, eg someone may talk too much, or another does not share his clue; some may ask others to talk/ summarise what the group has found etc.

The aim of the game is to help discussion skills and identify requirements necessary for a successful outcome. Your teacher/tutor will tell you who are timekeepers and who are observers.

Arrange yourselves in a circle. Your teacher/tutor will hand you a slip of paper containing one clue to help solve a murder mystery.

Rules

- You must not pass clues around or show them to anyone else.
- You must not walk round the group.
- The only way you may share clues and ideas is by talking.

Your teacher/tutor will make no suggestions.

By putting all the facts together, you will be able to solve the mystery. You must find the *murderer*, the *weapon*, the *time* of the murder, the *place* of the murder, and the *motive*. Once you think you know the answers as a group, let your teacher/tutor know and they will tell you if you are right. If you are not right, you will not be told which answers are wrong, only that some are wrong.

ACTIVITY 17 - FOR THE TEACHER/TUTOR

At the start of the activity you should indicate three or four students who will be observers as well as participants.

You should photocopy the clues below and cut them up, handing one (or more) to each student. If you have more students than clues, you will need to either make up some additional clues or ask students to share.

Clues

When he was discovered dead, Mr Green had a bullet hole in his thigh and a knife wound in his back.

Mr Brown shot at an intruder in his block of flats at midnight.

The lift attendant reported to the police that he saw Mr Green at 12.15am.

The bullet taken from Mr Green's thigh matched the gun owned by Mr Brown.

Only one bullet had been fired from Mr Brown's gun.

When the lift attendant saw Mr Green, Mr Green was bleeding slightly, but he did not seem very badly hurt.

A knife with Mr Green's blood on it was found in Miss Pink's garden.

The knife found in Miss Pink's garden had Mr White's fingerprints on it.

Mr Green had destroyed Mr Brown's business by stealing all his customers.

The lift attendant saw Mr Green's wife go to Mr White's flat at 11.30pm.

The lift attendant said that Mr Green's wife often left the building with Mr White.

Mr Green's body was found in the park.

Mr Green's body was found at 1.30am.

Mr Green had been dead for an hour when his body was found, according to a medical expert working with the police.

The lift attendant saw Mr Green go to Mr White's flat at 12.25am.

The lift attendant went off duty at 12.30am.

It was obvious from the condition of Mr Green's body that it had been dragged a long distance.

Miss Pink saw Mr Green go to Mr Brown's block of flats at 11.55pm.

Mr Green's wife disappeared after the murder.

The police were unable to find Mr White after the murder.

When the police tried to find Mr Brown after the murder, they discovered that he had disappeared.

The lift attendant said Miss Pink was in the hall of the block of flats when he went off duty.

Miss Pink often followed Mr Green.

Mr Brown had told Mr Green that he was going to kill him.

Miss Pink said nobody left the block of flats between 12.25am and 12.45am.

Mr Green's bloodstains were found in Mr White's car.

Mr Green's bloodstains were found on the carpet in the hall outside Mr Brown's flat.

ACTIVITY 18

BEHAVIOUR AND BARRIERS

Task 1

This activity is an individual evaluation of Activity 17, 'CSI-UK'.

The following bullet points will help in your evaluation and might help you identify behaviours that are barriers to communication, eg attempting to dominate conversation; aggressiveness; submissiveness; attitude; shyness etc.

- Was a leader needed? What was/might have been contributed by the leader?
- How was time lost in organising the group to solve the murder?
- How effective was the group when several people tried to talk at once? What alternatives were/might have been tried?
- What problems arose if some people did not positively attempt to contribute their clues?
- In what different ways did people ignore the clues of others?
- Did anyone encourage everyone to contribute his or her clues? If so, how was it done?
- Did anyone forget a clue and reach a wrong conclusion?
- Was everyone included in the discussion? (If anyone was excluded, how did that happen?)
- Did anyone take over the discussion? If so, why was that allowed? Did it do any harm? How could it have been prevented?
- What effect did the environment have on the management of the discussion?

Task 2

Having considered the session in the previous questions:

a) How would you now assess your own contribution? (Be prepared to recognise the positive as well as the negative aspects.)

b) How far was the role you played in this session typical of the way you operate in groups?

c) What changes (if any) do you intend to make?

ACTIVITY 19

MAKING ASSUMPTIONS

According to the story, after every Qantas Airlines flight the pilots complete a 'gripe sheet' that conveys to the ground crew engineers any mechanical problems on the aircraft during the flight (1). The engineer reads the form, corrects the problem, then writes details of action taken on the lower section of the form for the pilot to review before the next flight (2).

1) Something loose in cockpit.

2) Something tightened in cockpit.

1) Autopilot in altitude-hold mode produces a 200 feet-per-minute descent.

2) Cannot reproduce problem on ground.

1) Evidence of leak on right main landing gear.

2) Evidence removed.

1) Head phones volume unbelievably loud.

2) Head phones volume set to more believable level.

1) Friction locks cause throttle levers to stick.

2) That's what they're there for.

1) Suspected crack in windshield.

2) Suspect you're right.

1) Number 3 engine missing.

2) Engine found on right wing after brief search.

1) Aircraft handles funny.

2) Aircraft warned to straighten up, fly right, and be serious.

1) Target radar hums.

2) Reprogrammed target radar with lyrics.

From Alan Chapman's Businessballs site http://www.businessballs.com/stories.htm

These are supposedly real extracts from gripe forms completed by pilots with the solution responses by the engineers. It is clear from the examples that ground crew engineers have a keen sense of humour. It is also clear that the pilots have made assumptions about the ability of the engineers to interpret their observations regarding faults in the plane!

Now that you've (hopefully) enjoyed the extracts, write out the gripes so that they make sensible complaints, and the responses to make logical answers.

Incidentally, Qantas has the best safety record of all the world's major airlines.

ACTIVITY 20

INTEGRATED WORKFORCE AGENDA

The quality of a service is only as good as the people delivering it, so working together is a key aspect of health and social care policy, and workforce development is a major feature of successful partnership working.

To ensure successful working, barriers between people and organisations must be overcome and not be allowed to impede the provision of services and support.

What considerations should you make to ensure you work successfully with other professional people and organisations?

Working with a partner, devise a policy that could be implemented in your work placement to ensure that communications and interpersonal interactions are effective and encourage high-quality delivery of support and services for patients and service users.

You might need to consider:

- Job roles of workers
- Skills of workers
- Organisation plans – this might be a difficult area, but consider future developments that could be possible
- Changes in service delivery
- Service provision from other agencies
- Multi-disciplinary working
- Service provision from other agencies
- Multi-disciplinary working

KNOW HOW PATIENTS/SERVICE USERS MAY BE ASSISTED BY EFFECTIVE COMMUNICATION

ACTIVITY 21

TEXT FACILITIES

Do you have text facilities on your phone? How easy was it to use when you first got it? Do you use predictive text?

Find someone in your group who has a different make of mobile phone, or has not used a mobile phone like yours.

With their permission, exchange phones and send each other a text message explaining the reason that you chose your phone.

How easy is it to use a new phone? Could you describe the method to someone who is visually impaired?

Make an instruction leaflet that details 'how to send a text message'.

To ensure that your instructions are accurate, carry them out precisely!

ACTIVITY 22

PERSONAL COMMUNICATION PASSPORTS

Personal Communication Passports (PCPs) provide individual information about children or adults who cannot easily speak for themselves. The passports enable the holder's views and preferences to be recorded but are not 'static'; they provide ongoing, up-to-date information and can be used as a home/school liaison partnership.

PCPs are used to help other people get to know the holder and are widely used in care, health, education and social work settings.

Devise a Personal Communication Passport for an individual service user who has limited communication abilities. The passport should be attractive and should reflect the holder's character and describe their most effective means of communication.

ACTIVITY 23

THE NEEDS OF SERVICE USERS

In small groups, consider four service users who require support for their specific communication needs.

Devise a series of wall charts that illustrate and explain how their needs can be met using a variety of methods including technological means, eg devices that assist people to hear, speak, see.

You might need to research the Internet. Make a note of Internet sites that you use in order to reference them accurately.

ACTIVITY 24

MEETING NEEDS

Task 1

In small groups of three or four, use examples from your work placement and make notes that show how service users, key workers, relatives, support services etc are assisted by effective communication.

Task 2

Using the notes from task 1, explain how the examples support key legislation (data protection; equal rights etc).

Task 3

Put all the information from tasks 1 and 2 together in the format of a report suitable for use by the management. This will be used to provide evidence of the efficiency of the establishment.

You must include information regarding the various people and support services used, and should make certain that specific relevant legislation is conformed with, eg data protection, confidentiality, equal rights etc.

ACTIVITY 25

SUPPORT SERVICES

A variety of support services are used to help empower the communication skills of service users/patients.

In small groups of three or four, research the work of the following agencies:

Advocates; interpreters; translators; signers; counsellors; mentors; befrienders; psychologists; speech therapists.

Compare and contrast the work they do and the people they help.

Compile a frieze to go around the wall that informs others of the information you have found.

ACTIVITY 26

MAINTAINING CONFIDENTIALITY

Ensuring that effective communication is in place often means that comprehensive, personal records of service users/patients are stored, either electronically or in hard copy.

Task 1

On your own, investigate the rights of service users/patients with regards to:
- safe storage of their information
- protection of data
- patients'/service users' access to their own information
- the rights of workers to inform other workers/agencies of confidential information

Use textbooks, the library and the Internet. Make some notes for your own use.

57

Task 2

With a partner, and using the information you've both researched in task 1, compile a booklet for use by patients/service users and their families that explains these rights.

BE ABLE TO DEMONSTRATE OWN COMMUNICATION SKILLS IN A CARING ROLE

ACTIVITY 27

SUPPORT SERVICE USERS

To be a proficient carer you must have effective communication skills, both verbal and non-verbal. You must be able to support service users, their friends and relatives, and your co-workers.

One of the most horrific experiences in anyone's life is fire.

In this activity you must consider one of the following scenarios and design a resource pack that will inform and instruct to prevent harm occurring to people and limit damage to property. You must include some basic rules of escape, if a fire were to break out.

- You work in a residential nursing home that has two floors. There are two staircases and a lift, the kitchen is at the back of the building on the ground floor. The residents are all over 65 years old and have a range of physical disabilities and a number of the residents are wheelchair users.

- You are a student nurse sharing a house with four other students. The house is a mid-terrace, the back door leads to a walled yard that adjoins the back yard of the terraced house on the next street.

- You work in a large health centre which is staffed by a permanent team of receptionists and administrators. Doctors and health workers from all disciplines spend varying amounts of time in the centre. Of course, there are also patients as well as medical representatives and couriers etc who 'pop-in' to the centre on occasional business.

- You are a worker in a residential school for young people with sensory impairments. The school and residencies are all single-floor buildings spread over a large area.

The national Fire Escape Plan campaign, 'How Would You Get Out Alive?', is designed to encourage people to think about how they might escape from a fire.

1) Have an Escape Plan

2) If a Fire Has Started

3) If Your Escape Route is Blocked

4) Better That Fires Never Start!

Use the four pointers above to guide your project.

ACTIVITY 28

DEVELOPING COMMUNICATION SKILLS

Throughout this unit you have looked at a variety of areas that will encourage or impede good communication.

Devise an information leaflet that will guide workers in the health and social care sector to effective communication.

You must consider:

- Verbal communication, the advantages and disadvantages – when is verbal communication inappropriate?

- Techniques that enhance verbal communication – how can you interest listeners in what you have to say?

- Questioning – how can you use questions to stimulate the listener?
- Non-verbal communication (NVC) – how can use of NVC improve and develop a conversation?
- Listening skills – why are some people known as 'good listeners'? How can this skill be developed?

ACTIVITY 29

INTERACTING AS A CARER

In your role as a carer, make notes that will help in your preparation for a meeting with the parents or partner of a service user who you wish to commence using a Personal Communication Passport.

Areas for consideration might be:

- wishing to include photographs of family and friends
- inclusion of information, both past and present, that will help others understand the person and their character
- permissions.

ACTIVITY 30

INFLUENCES ON INTERACTIONS

Consider the meeting that is to take place for Activity 29. Write a report on factors that you think will have an influence on the interactions between you and the parents/partner.

How can you ensure that the meeting will be successful?

What factors will you try to avoid and what should be incorporated?

ACTIVITY 31

EFFECTIVE COMMUNICATION

You and your supervisor are to visit a young person with learning and communication difficulties who has moved into the area and will be attending school on a daily basis (as opposed to a residential basis).

You want to reassure all the family and have decided to put together a set of cards that will help you inform them about the activities carried out at the school.

You will need to research at least two of the many types of language that augment the spoken word, eg Braille; Makaton; Basic Sign Language etc.

ACTIVITY 32

THERAPIES

Play, drama and music can all be used when working with those who have difficulty communicating.

When using these areas of creative art, it is important that the workers give service users/patients the confidence to portray their ideas and feelings.

Research the work of music, art and drama therapists.

Put together a booklet that informs co-workers of the effectiveness of these therapies in supporting patients/service users.

ANSWERS

ACTIVITY 1

Sense	Example 1	Example 2
Sight	Watching a race from a distance	Lip reading
Sound	Hearing emotion in a voice, eg alarm	Mother 'cooing' to her baby to convey comfort
Smell	Some smells communicate information about the state of health, eg the 'pear drops' smell that might accompany diabetes	A scent that evokes a memory
Taste	Taste providing a warning of food that is 'off'	Taste as a mood enhancer
Touch	Demonstrating sympathy	Showing dislike

ACTIVITY 3

Type	Description
One to one	Doctor receiving and giving information
Formal	A written prescription ordering medication
Informal	Service users chatting
Formal instruction	'No Smoking' notice on the wall
Music playing	Calm and relaxing – or encouraging activity and stimulation

ACTIVITY 5

Examples of NVC that DO NOT support Professor Mehrabian's theory:

Email

Telephone calls

Notices

Memos

ACTIVITY 7

STATEMENT	POINT OF PROCESS
What do you want to communicate?	Aiming
Is the information prioritised?	Aiming
What would make the receiver interested?	Aiming
Who are you communicating with?	Aiming
What is the best way to communicate this?	Aiming
What language should I use?	Encoding

STATEMENT	POINT OF PROCESS
What assumptions am I making about the receiver?	Encoding
What might the receiver assume about me that will influence the communication?	Encoding
Will there be any distractions that will make communication difficult?	Transmitting
Can the receiver read/see/hear what you want to communicate?	Transmitting
Is what you are communicating consistent with the way you're saying/writing/showing it?	Transmitting
We think three times faster than we speak – it's easy for the speaker's words to get muddled with thoughts in our head.	Receiving
Ask for explanations.	Receiving
Ask for clarification – the responsibility of the message belongs to the sender, not the receiver.	Decoding
Ensure that no steps are missed out.	Responding

ACTIVITY 11

Abbreviation/ jargon/acronym	Could mean?	Actually means:
AIDS	Aid me! Help! Help!	Acquired Immune-Deficiency Syndrome
BP	Bed pan	Blood pressure
CABG	Cabbage	Coronary artery bypass graft
DAT	Baby talk – dis and dat	Drug Action Team
FPA	Feel pretty awful	Family Planning Association
GP	Generally poor	General Practitioner
MMR	Mine, mine – really!	Measles, mumps, rubella
NHS	Not healthy sis!	National Health Service
NICE	Nice one guys!	National Institute for Clinical Excellence
NKDA	Not known, didn't ask!	No known drug allergies
NRT	No race track	Nicotine Replacement Therapy
PALS	Pulling against library services	Patient Advice and Liaison Service
SSD	Special services device	Social Services Department
STI	Silent team initiative	Sexually Transmitted Infection
WHO	A rock band from the 70s	World Health Organisation

ACTIVITY 17

After receiving a superficial gunshot wound from Mr Brown, Mr Green went to Mr White's flat where he was killed by Mr White with a knife at 12.30am because Mr White was in love with Mr Green's wife.

After receiving a superficial gunshot wound from Mr Brown, Mr Green went to Mr White's flat where he was killed by Mr White with a knife at 12.30am because Mr White was in love with Mr Green's wife.

UNIT 3 – HEALTH, SAFETY AND SECURITY IN HEALTH AND SOCIAL CARE

This section focuses on: P1, P2, P3, P4, P5, P6, M1, M2, M3, D1, D2.

Introduction and learning outcomes

Health, safety and security should be central to all working experiences for both the worker and the service user; it is essential that you have a good understanding of potential hazards and of safety and security issues.

In health and social care situations, workers are responsible not only for the safety and security of themselves and their colleagues, but also for patients and service users who might not have the same degree of understanding or ability to take appropriate actions when required.

This unit will introduce you to health, safety and security issues in the health and social care workplace and will encourage you to consider potential hazards and how risks from them may be reduced.

1 Understand potential hazards in health and social care

2 Understand how legislation, guidelines, policies and procedures promote health, safety and security

3 Understand roles and responsibilities for health, safety and security in health and social care settings

4 Know how to deal with hazards in a local environment

Content

1) **Understand potential hazards in health and social care**

   Hazards; Working environment; Working practices; Risks; Incidents; Accidents.

2) **Understand how legislation, guidelines, policies and procedures promote health, safety and security**

   Legislation and guidelines; Policies and procedures; Health and social care service delivery.

3) **Understand roles and responsibilities for health, safety and security in health and social care settings**

   Roles; Responsibilities.

4) **Know how to deal with hazards in a local environment**

   Environments; Patient/service user group; Survey; Risks; Risk assessment; First-aid procedures.

Grading criteria

P1 use work placement experiences to explain a minimum of six potential hazards in a health or social care setting

P2 describe how key legislation in relation to health,

safety and security influences health and social care delivery

P3 using examples from work experience, describe how policies and procedures promote health, safety and security in the health and social care workplace

P4 examine the roles and responsibilities of key people in the promotion of health, safety and security in a health or social care setting

To meet P4 you will consider how the functions and jobs of key staff in health or social care settings enable them to keep staff and service users healthy, safe and secure.

P5 carry out a health and safety survey of a local environment used by a specific patient/service user group

P6 demonstrate basic first-aid skills

M1 explain how legislation, policies and procedures are used to promote the health, safety and security of individuals in the health and social care workplace

For M1 you will investigate how the law attempts to ensure that individuals in the health and social care setting are kept healthy, safe and secure.

M2 assess the risk associated with the use of the chosen local environment and make recommendations for change

To meet M2 you should weigh-up the risks that you have discovered in your health and safety survey (P5) and consider whether or not it is suitable for the user group.

M3 demonstrate first-aid skills on a critically injured individual

Using role-play you should carry out basic first-aid skills on an individual who has suffered serious injury, eg from a traffic accident; a fall from great height; been badly burnt in a fire.

D1 using examples from work experience, evaluate the effectiveness of policies and procedures for promoting health, safety and security

You will investigate the effectiveness of the strategies and actions taken at your workplace to ensure the workers and service users remain healthy, safe and secure.

D2 justify recommendations made for minimising the risks, as appropriate, for the setting and service user groups

To meet D2 you should give suggestions that will reduce the threats and dangers to service users who use the local environment from P5. You will need to give explanations for the suggestions that you make.

UNDERSTAND POTENTIAL HAZARDS IN HEALTH AND SOCIAL CARE

ACTIVITY 1

The Health and Safety Executive (HSE) is the body appointed to support and enforce health and safety law. They have defined two important concepts as follows:

- **Hazard:** 'a hazard is something with potential to cause harm'
- **Risk:** 'a risk is the likelihood of the hazard's potential being realised'

  Almost anything may be a hazard, but may or may not become a risk. For example:

- A trailing electric cable from a piece of equipment is a hazard. If it is trailing across a passageway, there is a high risk of someone tripping over it, but if it lies along a wall out of the way, the risk is much less.

- Toxic or flammable chemicals stored in a building are a hazard, and by their nature may present a high risk. However, if they are kept in a properly designed secure store, and handled by properly trained and equipped people, the risk is much less than if they are left about in a busy workshop for anyone to use – or misuse.

- A failed light bulb is a hazard. If it is just one bulb out of many in a room, it presents very little risk, but if it is the only light on a stairwell, it is a very high risk. Changing the bulb may be a high risk, if it is high up, or if the power has been left on, or low risk if it is in a table lamp which has been unplugged.

- A box of heavy material is a hazard. It presents a higher risk to someone who lifts it manually than if a mechanical handling device is properly used.

Task:

You are writing an episode for a television 'soap' based in a hospital, care home, day centre or health or social care setting of your choice.

Write a storyline using all the hazards above plus at least two more of your own devising.

ACTIVITY 2

CASE STUDIES – SERVICE USERS/PATIENTS

The reasons for a safe working environment seem obvious – no-one wants to be injured at work, or to see a service user hurt!

Mrs Joanne Brown is a resident in sheltered accommodation. She is a 72-year-old lady who is prone to falling and uses two walking sticks to assist her. Mrs Brown makes her own breakfast in her room each day; she has a small kitchen unit with a kettle, microwave, fridge and single ring electric cooker. She enjoys going into the garden whenever she can.

David Goldstein is 15, he lives in a home for young people with various disabilities – David was born with Down's Syndrome. He is very hard of hearing and uses a hearing aid in each ear. He also has learning difficulties. David's favourite occupation is painting but he will often try to help himself to materials from the store-cupboard!

Mrs Samina Hussain has recently moved in to a residential nursing home following a stroke which has left her with severe weakness down the left side of her body, she walks with difficulty and prefers to be pushed in a wheelchair. Mrs Hussain has a room on the ground floor of the home. The toilet is situated a few metres down the corridor.

Albert Brown lives by himself on the second floor of a block of flats. He has severe arthritis which gives him considerable pain and makes him bad-tempered. Care workers visit four times each day to help with personal hygiene (if he will allow) and with meal preparation, but Albert is often not at home as he likes to visit the local betting office and the pub.

Using a table similar to that below, identify and explain at least six potential hazards from the perspective of one of the individuals you have just read about.

Potential hazard	Reason for occurrence

ACTIVITY 3

CASE STUDIES – WORKERS

Having examined potential hazards from the perspective of the service user, now consider potential hazards from the perspective of the worker in health or social care.

Ambreen is a care worker in a residential nursing home. She works a shift rota that includes night duties. The home is on two floors with a lift and two staircases – a key-code is required to open doors to the staircases. Ambreen's duties include personal care for residents and some snack preparation as required.

Phil is a staff-nurse in a large accident and emergency department. Phil works a four week rota system that includes night duties. He is often the senior nurse in charge, so his duties include some administrative work that he really does not enjoy!

Lin-Yau is a part-time receptionist in a health centre, her duties include telephone answering, typing the doctor's letters, making appointments – in fact, Lin-Yau spends most of her time working with the computer.

Sheila works full time in the kitchens of a large nursing home. Her working day starts at 07.00 when she prepares breakfast for the residents. Sheila has a small team of workers to assist in meal preparation and kitchen duties; she is also responsible for running the kitchen, ordering supplies and managing her staff.

Imelda is a community care worker. She loves her work which involves visiting a variety of service users each day. Imelda's duties differ with each client that she visits. Some people need assistance with dressing and personal hygiene and others require help with meal preparation.

Create a table like the one below and write in your ideas

Potential hazard	Reason for occurrence

ACTIVITY 4

CASE STUDIES – POINTS!

Work in small groups of four to six students.

Give yourself one point for each hazard that you have identified in both of the case studies.

Present your case studies and answers for consideration by the rest of your group – those who identify additional hazards in your case study will gain an extra two points for each.

Make notes of all your findings.

You might have included some of the following:

Back injuries – physical abuse – needlestick injury – repetitive strain injury (RSI) – falls – headaches – burns – chemical damage – choking etc.

In your group, each student should select a different hazard and research the occurrence of that hazard. You might use the Internet to help find statistics; ensure that you make a note of the website address so that you can find it again easily.

If you are having difficulty finding information, try the following websites:

Health and Safety Executive

http://www.hse.gov.uk/statistics/industry/healthservices.htm

The Royal Society for the Prevention of Accidents

http://www.rospa.com/

ACTIVITY 5

RISK ASSESSMENT (1)

Scenario:

All workplaces that have five or more employees must carry out and record risk assessments (more on this in Activity 22). Specialist risk assessments are carried out in the homes of service users to ensure that accidents do not happen to the service user or to the carer (more on this in Activity 22).

Devise a risk assessment for one of the workers in Activity 2.

ie

Residential nursing home

Accident and Emergency unit

Health centre

Kitchen

Community

Give reasons for each risk that you include.

When devising your risk assessment, you might consider the following:

Step 1

Identify the hazards.

Step 2

Decide who might be harmed and how.

Step 3

Evaluate the risks and decide on precautions.

Step 4

Record your findings and implement them.

Step 5

Review your assessment and update if necessary.

These are steps that the Health and Safety Executive (HSE) recommend (more on this in Activity 22).

ACTIVITY 6

RISK ASSESSMENT (2)

Risk assessments are also carried out for 'one-off events' to minimise accidents etc.

Using the five steps from Activity 5, and the service users and workers from Activities 2 and 3, devise risk assessments, justifying each risk, for the following:

- David and his friends go to the local bowling centre for the evening.
- Sheila does the shopping for the nursing home.
- Albert is taken on his first visit to the local community day centre (being collected by a worker).
- Samina Hussain goes on a shopping trip to a large undercover precinct/mall (eg White Rose Centre; Bluewater; Meadow Hall; Metro Centre; Trafford Centre; McArthur Glen etc).
- Joanne Brown visits the local horticultural gardens escorted by a carer and the Country Ranger.

ACTIVITY 7

Lin-Yau started working as a part-time receptionist very recently. She will now undertake an Induction training course with other new employees from health centres or GP surgeries in the local area.

Devise a training package that includes the health, safety and security needs of workers in health centres and general practitioner surgeries. (You might not be aware of all the requirements, but there are some areas that will be appropriate to all workers.)

Questions and issues that you might include:

Can you name your boss/line manager?

How does your job fit in with the rest of the organisation?

Can you find the first-aid facilities?

Who is the first-aider?

Manual handling – remember nearly everyone has to lift something.

How do you deal with rude or aggressive service users/patients?

ACTIVITY 8

WORKING CONDITIONS – ORGANISATIONS

Consider the following paragraph. Write your answers out as a short discussion.

Of the many hazards found in working environments, gases and chemicals are common – an issue that has recently hit the headlines is that of smoking.

How can workers in health and social care ensure that their working environment is free from this hazard – without denying service users/patients their right to make choices about smoking?

ACTIVITY 9

WORKING CONDITIONS – AT HOME

A tragic accident occurred to 18-year-old Lee resulting in paraplegia and wheelchair use.

A flat has been found and is to be converted so that it will be suitable for a wheelchair user. The services of an occupational therapist, a surveyor and an environmental health officer have been employed to give final approval for the flat design.

Your task is to put yourself in the place of Lee. You must consider all aspects of life and make a scale drawing of the flat and of each room, furnishing and equipping them to ensure that the flat will enable you to live life to its fullest while ensuring that hazards are overcome and accidents are unlikely to occur.

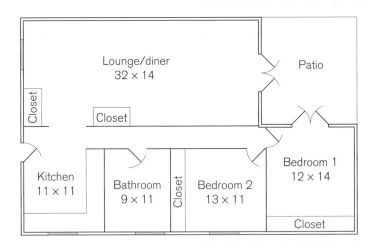

ACTIVITY 10

ACCIDENTS

Falls are a major cause of disability and one of the biggest causes of mortality from injury in older people in the UK. Five percent of falls result in fractures, with an increased risk for those with osteoporosis. The long-term implications of falling include possible physical disability, entry into long-term care, and psychological problems.

(Health Survey For England 2005)

The staff in the nursing home where you have been working have recently noticed a rise in the number of residents who are falling.

Research the causes of falls in the elderly.

Design a questionnaire that could be used to investigate the reason for the falls.

Write a report that could explain the increase in this type of accident in the nursing home.

In small groups, compare your reports and make suggestions that might reduce the number of falls experienced.

UNDERSTAND HOW LEGISLATION, GUIDELINES, POLICIES AND PROCEDURES PROMOTE HEALTH, SAFETY AND SECURITY

Introduction to the Health and Safety at Work Act 1974

The Health and Safety at Work Act 1974 sets out the general duties which employers have towards employees and members of the public, and employees have to themselves and to each other.

These duties are qualified in the Act by the principle of 'so far as is reasonably practicable'. In other words, an employer does not have to take measures to avoid or reduce the risk if they are technically impossible or if the time, trouble or cost of the measures would be grossly disproportionate to the risk.

What the law requires here is what good management and common sense would lead employers to do anyway: that is, to look at what the risks are and take sensible measures to tackle them.

Amongst other things, the Act seeks to secure the health, safety and welfare of people whilst they work and protect other people against risks to health or safety arising from the activity of people at work.

ACTIVITY 11

LEGISLATION, GUIDELINES AND POLICIES

Before you can start exploring how legislation, policies and guidelines work in the health or social care sector, you must understand and be able to use the terms.

Research the three terms:

Legislation

Guidelines

Policies

Find a definition for each one.

Select one example of each – legislation, guideline, policy – from your work placement and explain why it falls into that category.

ACTIVITY 12

YOUR RESPONSIBILITY

The Health and Safety at Work Act 1974 imposes general duties on everybody connected with work – not just the employers.

Very briefly, the Act states that:

- **Employers**

Section 2(1) Ensure the health, safety and welfare of employees while at work.

- **Employees**

Section 7 (a-b) it shall be the duty of every employee while at work:

■ To take reasonable care for the health and safety of himself and others who may be affected by his acts or omissions at work.

■ To co-operate with his employer or any other person, so far as is necessary, to enable his employer or other person to perform or comply with any requirement or duty imposed under a relevant statutory provision.

Thinking of your own work placement, how are the duties of the employer and the employee met?

Write an information leaflet that informs workers of the duties of employers and employees and could be used as part of the new employee induction training.

ACTIVITY 13

MANAGEMENT OF HEALTH AND SAFETY AT WORK REGULATIONS 1999 (MHSW)

The MHSW acts in conjunction with the Health and Safety at Work Act and specifies the core duties of employers and employees. Research the MHSW. What impact has it had on your workplace?

Discuss with your employer or tutor the implications for employers and for employees.

Document your findings in the form of a flier or handout.

For a fact sheet on Management of Health and Safety at Work Regulations go to the following website:

http://www.lhc.org.uk/members/pubs/factsht/67fact.htm

ACTIVITY 14

HEALTH AND SAFETY AT WORK

You have been asked by your employer to investigate your workplace with a view to drawing up codes of policy for each area.

You have looked at the leaflet 'Health and Safety Regulation, a short guide' published by the HSE. (available on http://www.hse.gov.uk/pubns/hsc13.pdf)

You have decided that this will be a large task and you should enlist the help of up to four co-workers, dividing the workplace into sections, allocating one section to yourself and one to each of your colleagues:

■ Kitchen and dining rooms

■ Reception area and offices

■ Bathrooms and toilets

■ Staircases, lifts, storage areas

■ Service users/patients

Each person is to devise a Code of Practice that considers risks and advises on sensible measures to avoid them.

The completed Codes of Practice should be presented to the whole group for comments and discussion.

ACTIVITY 15

Case study

Twilight Nursing Home was built in 1995, on two floors. It has a modern look and appears a light and airy building.

The home caters for people with physical difficulties and dementia. Those with physical difficulties have their own bedroom on the ground floor, and those with dementia have rooms on the first floor.

The foyer is open and welcoming. The secretary's office has a window that opens into the foyer, and the visitor's book is placed on a table in the foyer to be signed on entry and exit. Visitors are encouraged throughout the day, although it is preferred that they do not visit during meal times.

Residents with dementia are unable to exit the building unless accompanied by a member of staff, as the first floor doors are kept closed and must be opened with a code – for ease of access for visitors the code is posted on the outside of the door.

Smoking is discouraged on the premises – there are smoke and fire alarms throughout the building as required.

About three months ago, Josie, one of the care workers, spilt boiling water from the kettle over her hand and was 'off sick' for two weeks. The manager of the home thought that the incident should be reported using the RIDDOR legislation. However, when Imran, one of the night staff, was attacked by a resident with dementia, it was decided by both Imran and the management that it would not be in the best interests of the resident to report the incident. Imran was away from work for three weeks.

To ensure the home complies with legislation, all medication is kept securely stored. Cleaning products are kept in cupboards on each floor.

Julie, the secretary, was given the task of preparing plans and procedures to deal with accidents, incidents and emergencies involving hazardous substances, but as all the drugs are locked away and the chemicals are in cupboards, this was considered unnecessary.

The kitchens are on the ground floor, and Sheila, the senior member of the catering staff, has a certificate in Food Safety and Hygiene. All the food is kept at the correct temperature and in safe storage. Recently a compost heap has been introduced in the garden, just round the corner from the rear entrance to the kitchens. This enables the kitchen staff to dispose of food waste.

Residents' records are kept as paper documents in ring binders on the shelf in the staff office. The nursing staff ensures records are updated regularly, to ensure continuity of information and communication.

Twilight Nursing Home complied with all the relevant legislation when it was built, but additional legislation has been introduced and it could be that some areas do not meet the required standards.

Read the case study carefully, identify areas that fail to meet the regulations and make suggestions, supported by legislation, which would ensure the home will pass any future inspection.

UNDERSTAND ROLES AND RESPONSIBILITIES FOR HEALTH, SAFETY AND SECURITY IN HEALTH AND SOCIAL CARE SETTINGS

ACTIVITY 16

KEY LEGISLATION AT WORK

Your employer has asked you to devise a grid that will enable staff to identify responsibilities they have with regard to application of legislation.

The grid should be suitable to pin up in the staff room.

Your grid could look like the one below, or you might have your own ideas of how it should look.

	Food Safety Regulations (General Food Hygiene) 1995	Food Safety Act 1990	Manual Handling Operations Regulations 1992	RIDDOR 1995	Data Protection Act 1998	Management of Health and Safety at Work Regulations 1999	COSHH 2002
Matron/ Supervisor							
Kitchen staff							
Porter							
Receptionist							
Telephonist							
Careworkers							
Etc							

ACTIVITY 17

TRAINING AND DEVELOPMENT

Your workplace has implemented a series of training activities which include health, safety and security.

You have been asked to present an illustrated talk that considers one of the issues listed below:

- safe storage and use of equipment and materials in all areas of your workplace
- dealing with spillage of hazardous and non-hazardous materials; and disposing of waste immediately and safely
- correct manual handling procedures and techniques
- completing health, safety and security records.

Examples of poor or good practice should be illustrated.

Relevant statistics could be used.

Following the presentation, a summary of your talk should be made available for display in poster format.

nb you might find the following websites useful:

Workplace Health Connect

http://www.workplacehealthconnect.co.uk/

Health and Safety Executive

http://www.hse.gov.uk/statistics/industry/healthservices.htm

The Royal Society for the Prevention of Accidents

http://www.rospa.com/

ACTIVITY 18

MEDIA HUNT

Spend a week collecting information on work-related accidents and illnesses that occur in health and social care settings.

You should look at:

- national and local newspapers
- television and radio articles
- journals and magazines
- any other sources you can think of.

Ensure that you note the source of your information so you could return to the document at a later date.

Divide your information into categories. These could be related to age; accident or illness; gender; workers; service users/patients etc.

Compile an information portfolio that could be presented to support further work.

ACTIVITY 19

SECURITY PROCEDURES 1

Carry out an assessment of a health or social care setting with a view to devising a code of practice that informs readers how to make the setting secure for both staff and service users.

The assessment should indicate how unwanted visitors could be prevented from gaining access.

In preparation for the assessment you will need to develop a list of questions/ statements.

ACTIVITY 20

SECURITY PROCEDURES 2

Using the assessment from Activity 19, develop a code of practice that could be implemented in your workplace, for the benefit of staff and service users/patients.

The code of practice should be linked to specific legislation and should be written up as an information bulletin to be put up in the staff office.

ACTIVITY 21

RESPECTING OTHERS

Recent reports indicate that NHS and other healthcare workers can be as much as four times more likely to experience work-related violence and aggression than other workers.

Following their success in other areas of the country your employer has decided to introduce a 'zero tolerance' policy to combat an increase in aggression in your area.

You have been asked to design a series of posters to raise staff and public awareness of this policy while respecting the needs, wishes, preferences and choices of individuals.

You must first research:

- the most common types of incident

■ the factors that create a risk.

You should then compile a report that indicates appropriate steps that employers and employees might take to deal with verbal and physical abuse.

nb The website of The National Audit Office UK might provide useful information, as might the website of The Health and Safety Executive.

KNOW HOW TO DEAL WITH HAZARDS IN A LOCAL ENVIRONMENT

ACTIVITY 22

RISK ASSESSMENT

Employers are legally required to assess the risks of their workplace(s).

Accidents and ill health can ruin lives and affect business, so employers are required to assess the risks and put in place plans to control those risks.

You don't have to be a health-and-safety expert to prepare a risk assessment form. Risk assessment is simply a careful examination of what, at work, could cause harm to people. Assessment involves weighing-up whether enough precautions have been taken to prevent harm. Workers and others have a right to be protected from harm caused by a failure to take reasonable control measures.

Research the Risk Assessment Process; you will find resources to assist you on the Internet (www.hse.gov.uk). Make a file of the information that you find, index the contents and write an introduction to the work.

Then conduct a risk assessment of your college/centre/work placement or your own home.

ACTIVITY 23

ENVIRONMENTS

Choose an environment that you visit – this might be a park, a shopping precinct, a restaurant etc.

Devise a list of risks and hazards; identify the potential danger that might be caused; evaluate the risks and decide on the precautions that could be taken.

Using the information that you gained from Activity 22, put your findings into a suitable risk assessment form – or a form that you have devised.

ACTIVITY 24

A DAY OUT

You and your work colleagues are taking a group of children from the local school on a day trip to a nearby theme park. This will involve a 40-minute bus journey. You will be accompanied by staff from the school and volunteer helpers.

Indicate the activities in which the group might participate.

Design an assessment form that will specify any risks to health or safety at the theme park.

Write a letter that will be sent to parents, carers and guardians before the trip, justifying recommendations for minimising risks, eg explanations regarding rides or activities that will or will not be accessible to the children.

ACTIVITY 25

HOLIDAYS

Some of the staff from the residential home where you are on work placement are taking a group of residents with learning difficulties on a one-week holiday to a seaside centre designed for those with similar requirements and needs. You are accompanying the group and have been asked to devise risk assessments for the bus journey which involves six hours' travelling.

ACTIVITY 26

FIRST-AID – ROLE-PLAY

Working in groups of three – one casualty, two carers – students should devise emergency situations that could be used to demonstrate to year 8 and 9 pupils, specific first-aid procedures. The follow-up process of recording information and record keeping should also be demonstrated. Here are some suggestions:

- A child with a bleeding nose
- A small child with wasp stings
- A footballer who has fallen on a piece of glass
- An elderly person who has fallen and hurt his legs
- A teenager having an asthma attack for the first time
- A waitress who has scalded her arm under the steam machine
- A baby who is having a fit

ACTIVITY 27

FIRST-AID

You have been asked by your work placement manager to give a talk and demonstration to the rest of the staff regarding the basics of first-aid and life saving procedures.

You will need to devise a series of illustrated leaflets or posters that explain the following terms, and describe how they should be dealt with by the first-aider:

- Action at the scene of an emergency
- Triage
- Haemorrhage
- Choking
- Heart attack
- Drowning

ANSWERS

ACTIVITY 11

Legislation – is law which has been promulgated (made official) by Parliament or other governing body.

Guidelines – outlines or indications, of acceptable conduct or procedure.

Policies – plans embracing the general goals and acceptable procedures of an organisation.

ACTIVITY 15

There could be lapses in security as there does not appear to be a process to ensure visitors to the home are who they say they are – unwanted visitors could enter quite easily.

Legislation to be addressed includes:

- Management of Health and Safety at Work Regulations 1999
- Data Protection Act 1998
- RIDDOR 1995
- COSHH 2002
- Food Safety (General Food Hygiene) Regulations 1995
- (Residential care homes will be exempt from the Smoking Ban introduced throughout the UK in 2007)

UNIT 4 – DEVELOPMENT THROUGH THE LIFE STAGES

This section focuses on: P1, P2, P3, P4, P5, M1, M2, M3, D1, D2.

Introduction and learning outcomes

You might have decided that you wish to work in the health or social care sector, but have you considered a particular age group or sector of society that you would like to work with?

This unit will introduce you to different life stages and influences on growth and development.

As someone who wishes to work in the health or social care sector, it is important that you can reflect on the consequence of major life events that affect the development of individuals and that you have considered the nature-nurture debate.

1 Understand human growth and development through the life stages

2 Understand how life factors and events may influence the development of the individual

3 Understand physical changes and psychological perspectives in relation to ageing

Contents

Grading criteria

P1 describe physical, intellectual, emotional and social development through the life stages

P2 describe the potential influences of five life factors on the development of individuals

P3 describe the influence of two predictable and two unpredictable major life events on the development of the individual

P4 describe two theories of ageing

P5 describe physical and psychological changes due to the ageing process

M1 discuss the nature-nurture debate in relation to individual development

To cover this criterion you should examine the debate around the influence of heredity and genetics, and the environment and upbringing (socialisation), on development of the individual.

M2 explain how major life events can influence the development of the individual

Give details of how important events can control or change the development of the individual.

M3 use examples to compare two major theories of ageing

To meet M3 you should investigate examples of ageing. Theorists disagree about the process of getting old. Is it 'normal' to remain active? Or is it more usual to withdraw from activities and social life?

D1 evaluate the nature-nurture debate in relation to development of the individual

Analyse and assess the influences of heredity and the environment/socialisation on development of the individual.

D2 evaluate the influence of two major theories of ageing on health and social care provision

You will need to compare and contrast two theories of ageing and say how you think health and care provision is affected by ageing.

UNDERSTAND HUMAN GROWTH AND DEVELOPMENT THROUGH THE LIFE STAGES

ACTIVITY 1

THREADS OF DEVELOPMENT

Devise a table – you might like to use the one below or devise one of your own.

Complete the table to show the basic characteristics of development that occur during that period.

You should find that the boxes do not fill equally!

SUMMARY OF THREADS OF DEVELOPMENT

STAGE DEVELOPMENT	0-3 Years Birth & Infancy	4-9 Years Childhood	10-18 Years Adolescence	19-65 Years Adulthood	65+ Years Older adulthood	Final stages of life
Physical						
Intellectual						
Emotional						
Social						

ACTIVITY 2

DEFINITIONS

You probably found that when completing the first column of boxes in the previous activity you ran out of room!

More development occurs during the first five years of life than at any other time, but growth occurs at every stage of life from conception to very old age.

Look at the picture and write a brief paragraph for each person.

You must try to use the words or phrases in your writing showing that you understand the meaning of the words:

Growth	Development	Developmental norms	Life course
Maturation	Life expectancy	Physical	Intellectual
Language	Emotional	Social	Change along the continuum of life
Potential causes and effects of delayed development	Holistic development	Cognitive	Communication

ACTIVITY 3

WHO AM I?

We all develop in an holistic manner. Aspects of our development, whether emotional, social, cognitive, physical and spiritual, are interdependent and of equal importance.

On a piece of paper, represent your life. Do this in a way that has most meaning for you. You might choose to note down important stages and landmarks in your life. You can draw shapes and use colours which reflect important aspects of your life, including places, objects, people and ideas that have influenced you. You might like to do intricate, colourful drawings, or prefer to draw simple lines or to write notes. You can use large sheets of coloured paper, or you might prefer standard A4 white. The important thing is to ensure that it is your personal lifeline which is represented.

Ensure that you include the following:

- aspects of development that you might have to research (when you first walked; first tooth; first words etc)
- age when you started school
- important people who came in to your life – friends, relatives, neighbours, teachers etc
- significant events that influenced you, eg owning a pet; moving house; death of a favourite grandparent etc
- sensory impacts on your life; particular smells, tastes, beautiful scenes, music etc
- illness that meant you missed school or had to go to hospital

When you have completed your lifeline, you should see how a variety of factors have contributed to make you the person you are.

Imagine the future when you have successfully completed your BTEC and made your way in life to achieve fame and fortune – the media are vying for your story. Write an article that describes and explains who you are and how you became such a well-rounded person!

ACTIVITY 4

REQUIREMENTS FOR DEVELOPMENT

Proper nutrition, health care, and stimulation improve learning and other abilities not only during the early years but throughout life.

In small groups, each person should select one of the life stages that you looked at in Activity 1. Put together a plan to meet the needs of nutrition, health care and stimulation for that life stage.

The plan can take the form of a poster or large diagram.

If your group is too small to cover all of the life stages, work together to ensure you complete the age-range. (Life stage groups: Pregnancy; 0–3yrs; 4–9yrs; 10–18yrs; 19–65yrs; 65+ yrs; final stages of life).

ACTIVITY 5

CONCEPTION AND FOETAL DEVELOPMENT

The first 12 weeks of pregnancy are critical in the development of a baby, as it is during this time that all essential external and internal structures are formed. It is for this reason that all harmful substances must be avoided, including alcohol and tobacco.

The table below gives you a day-by-day account of how a baby develops over the first 12 weeks of pregnancy.

The first twelve weeks of pregnancy

	Day 1	Day 2	Day 3	Day 4	Day 5	Day 6	Day 7
Week One	First day of last period	Menstrual phase complete					
	Ovarian Follicle begins to develop						

	Day 8	Day 9	Day 10	Day 11	Day 12	Day 13	Day 14
Week Two	Completion of development of follicle					Called on Oocyte	Ovulation Occurs

	Day 15	Day 16	Day 17	Day 18	Day 19	Day 20	Day 21
Week Three	Fertilisation Bingo !!!	Cell division starts	Cell division rapid	Early blastocyst	Late blastocyst	Implantation begins	

	Day 22	Day 23	Day 24	Day 25	Day 26	Day 27	Day 28
Week Four	Placenta begins to form		Implantation completed	Primitive placental circulation	Sac develops around baby	Placenta fully functional	Now called an embryo

	Day 29	Day 30	Day 31	Day 32	Day 33	Day 34	Day 35
Week Five	First missed period	Pregnancy test may be positive from here on		Nervous system begins to develop as the spinal column takes shape and the brain begins to develop			Heart begins to develop

	Day 36	Day 37	Day 38	Day 39	Day 40	Day 41	Day 42
Week Six	Heart starts to beat	Eye and ear cells present	Length 2.0mm	Optic pits develop	Arm buds develop	Leg buds develop	Length 4.0mm

	Day 43	Day 44	Day 45	Day 46	Day 47	Day 48	Day 49
Week Seven	Length 5.0mm	Eyes continue to develop	Nose and mouth start forming	Hand plates present	Length 7.0mm	Limbs continue to grow	Length 8.0mm

	Day 50	Day 51	Day 52	Day 53	Day 54	Day 55	Day 56
Week Eight	Oral and nasal cavities develop	Length 9.0mm	Upper lip formed	Length 10.0mm	Arms bent at elbows	Fingers noticeable	Length 13.0mm

	Day 57	Day 58	Day 59	Day 60	Day 61	Day 62	Day 63
Week Nine	Length 16.0mm	Eyelids begin forming	Toes start developing	Length 17.0mm	Genitals and anus forming		Length 18.0mm

	Day 64	Day 65	Day 66	Day 67	Day 68	Day 69	Day 70
Week Ten	Arms longer and bent at elbows	Testes and ovaries developing	Facial features present	Not able to distinguish between male and female yet	Genitals continue to develop	Not able to distinguish between male and female yet	Heart begins to develop

	Day 71	Day 72	Day 73	Day 74	Day 75	Day 76	Day 77
Week Eleven	Now called a foetus from here on to the end of the pregnancy		The foetus is now bigger than the placenta. The sac around the baby fills with fluid to allow the growing baby to move around		External genitals continue to form. The foetus can now respond to light, noise and pressure.		Length 50mm

	Day 78	Day 79	Day 80	Day 81	Day 82	Day 83	Day 84
Week Twelve	Face has human profile			Genitals have distinguishable male and female characteristics but are still not fully formed			Length 61mm

As you can see, nearly all the development has taken place by 12 weeks of pregnancy. For the rest of the pregnancy, organs will mature and develop and the baby will continue to grow in size.

Before you move on to the next activity, identify words in the chart that are new to you – some you might have come across in Unit 5 (the anatomy and physiology unit).

Research the meanings of the following words to complete the table below.

Word	Meaning
Foetus	
Embryo	
Oocyte	
Ovarian follicle	
Blastocyst	
Placenta	
Optic pits	

ACTIVITY 6

PREGNANCY

Pregnancy is divided into three sections or trimesters. You have already considered the developmental events throughout trimester one, now look at the statements below from the second and third trimesters. Put them into the correct weeks of development in a table, copied from p.83. Some have been completed to help you get started.

The heartbeat is strong and the body is growing fast to catch up with the well-developed head. Eyes are still tightly closed beneath sealed eyelids and the foetus is making 'rooting' movements ready to search for milk after birth.

The foetus can look from side to side, hear loud music or shouting, and distinguish sweet tastes from bitter ones. If she/he starts doing acrobatics just as the mother is dropping off to sleep, it could be because when resting she (the mother) breathes more deeply, with the result that the oxygen supply to the foetus increases.

The foetus resembles a miniature human being and is about as heavy as a 50p coin. Nipples appear and (if a girl) a uterus, cervix and vagina form. If the baby is a boy, a penis is visible. Even as early as 13 weeks, the baby may find and suck his/her thumb.

The eyebrows and lashes are starting to grow, the eyes have moved from the sides to the front of the head, and the ears have moved up from the neck to the head. The intestines are developing folds to absorb nutrients more efficiently.

Permanent teeth are already forming buds behind the milkteeth buds in the jaw. The arms and legs are now in the same proportions that they'll be at birth. As the nerves and muscles develop the foetus can control her/his movements, and may bend an elbow or frown.

The bones are hardening and tiny nails appear. Blood vessels show through the translucent skin, which is now covered in fine, downy hair called lanugo. By now, the foetus weighs about the same as a small pot of yoghurt. **week 16**

With plenty of room to kick and roll around, the baby is very active. She/he's starting to lay down 'brown fat' around the kidneys, chest and the back of the neck, to help regulate temperature in the first weeks after the birth.

The foetus has a big forehead and the eyes are sensitive to light. Hearing is sufficiently good for her/him to respond to loud noises and the mother's heartbeat can be heard.

Vital organs are now mature but the lungs aren't ready to cope with independent breathing. If labour started now special care would be required. Any baby born at or after this time is considered 'viable' because it has a chance of surviving.

The skin is starting to thicken into four layers and a creamy, moisturising substance called vernix covers it. She/he measures about 25cm from top to bottom.

The foetus looks very much how she/he will when born – although the skin is quite red and wrinkled, and more fat stores will be laid down over the next few weeks. There are even lines on the fingers – fingerprints!

Antibodies are being transferred from the mother's blood to the foetus, to protect from infection during the early months of life. Taste buds are forming on the tongue, and water and sugars can be absorbed from the amniotic fluid. **week 21**

She/he has rapid eye movements during sleep, just like you when you're dreaming. She/he measures around 40.5cm from head to bottom, but if she/he were born now she'd/he'd still need special care. **week 32**

Airways are developing and the foetus is moving regularly. Babies kick most vigorously before week 30, after which space becomes more restricted, and all this activity helps their muscles develop.

The brain is bigger and amazingly complex, the lungs are maturing in preparation for the first breath and the irises are starting to dilate.

She/he's probably settled into the birth position and the midwife can tell you which way she/he's going to be born. Head downwards is the norm, but some babies remain in a breech position and a few lie across the uterus.

Fluid is passing through the foetus's kidneys and is recycled back into the amniotic fluid. She/he's drawing on the mother's calcium reserves to harden her/his bones, so she/he needs to eat plenty of calcium-rich foods.

She/he's going through a rapid growth phase and may gain up to 227g ($\frac{1}{2}$lb) a week. Through the wall of the mother's stomach the open eyes can differentiate between darkness and light. **week 35**

The hearing is increasingly acute, the nails are growing and she/he may be born with a full head of hair. She/he weighs about 5 $\frac{1}{2}$lbs (2.5kg) and measures 46cm from head to bottom.

She/he's still laying down fat stores and will almost double in weight before birth. The creamy moisturiser and fine, downy hair on the body are beginning to disappear and the lungs are producing surfactant, a substance that will help them to inflate more easily after birth.

The finger and toenails are now complete, which means that she/he is considered clinically mature, though she/he'll continue to gain about 28g a day. A boy's testicles will have descended from his abdomen into his scrotum.

The body is about 33cm long from head to bottom. The amniotic fluid cushions and protects the foetus against Braxton Hicks Contractions. **week 30**

Growth slows down in the last week or two.

Some antibodies are passing from the mother through the placenta into the bloodstream to give the immune system a boost for the first six months while it matures. The bowel contains meconium – a sticky, tar-like substance that will be excreted as the first poo soon after birth. **week 39**

She/he is becoming plumper so the skin, which is gradually thickening, looks smoother and more opaque. Eyelashes are formed and the eyes will open this week. Virtually all babies are born with blue or dark blue eyes and it's not until some weeks after birth that they become the colour they'll stay. **week 26**

She/he may suck her/his thumb, and already has a preference for using the right or left hand. She/he can hear and might even recognise the mother's voice.

She/he's plump, mature and finally ready for life outside the uterus. She/he's roughly 51cm long, though of course newborn babies vary greatly in size and weight.

The heart rate is around 120 to 160 beats per minute, roughly twice the speed of yours. If born prematurely there would be a fair chance of survival, although problems with breathing and keeping warm would mean special care would be required.

Week	Development
13	
14	
15	
16	The bones are hardening and tiny nails appear. Blood vessels show through the translucent skin, which is now covered in fine, downy hair called lanugo. By now, the foetus weighs about the same as a small pot of yoghurt.
17	
18	
19	
20	
21	Antibodies are being transferred from the mother's blood to the foetus, to protect from infection during the early months of life. Taste buds are forming on the tongue, and water and sugars can be absorbed from the amniotic fluid.
22	
23	
24	
25	
26	She/he is becoming plumper so the skin, which is gradually thickening, looks smoother and more opaque. Eyelashes are formed and the eyes will open this week. Virtually all babies are born with blue or dark blue eyes and it's not until some weeks after birth that they become the colour they'll stay.
27	
28	
29	
30	The body is about 33cm long from head to bottom. The amniotic fluid cushions and protects the foetus against Braxton Hicks Contractions.
31	
32	She/he has rapid eye movements during sleep, just like you when you're dreaming. She/he measures around 40.5cm from head to bottom, but if she/he were born now she'd/he'd still need special care.
33	
34	
35	She/he's going through a rapid growth phase and may gain up to 227g (½lb) a week. Through the wall of the mother's stomach the open eyes can differentiate between darkness and light.
36	
37	
38	
39	Some antibodies are passing from the mother through the placenta into the bloodstream to give the immune system a boost for the first six months while it matures. The bowel contains meconium – a sticky, tar-like substance that will be excreted as the first poo soon after birth.
40	

ACTIVITY 7

MILESTONES OF DEVELOPMENT

As you saw in Activity 1, we do not all develop at the same rate. However, we tend to follow the same sequence and achieve stages of behaviour or activity in the same order – these stages are called 'milestones'.

Design a series of illustrated posters to be placed in the local health centre to inform parents and carers of the physical and cognitive development of a child from birth to five years.

You will see that more development takes place in these five years than in any other five year period of life!

ACTIVITY 8

POTENTIAL CAUSES AND EFFECTS OF DELAYED DEVELOPMENT

How well and how 'early' or 'late' we achieve milestones dictate whether or not we are on target for 'normal' or for 'delayed' development.

You are probably aware of many causes of delayed development and of the effects they might have in life, eg the rubella virus (German Measles) can cause deafness.

For this activity you will **work in small groups** to produce information sheets that investigate the causes and effects of delayed development.

Start by dividing the work into the following sections:

Birth weight

Physical development and movement

Cognitive development

Language and communication

Emotional and social development

Research the causes of delayed development in each of the sections, and the effect they will have on future development.

You should consider that the information sheets will be for display in the classroom to inform a group of students on a cadet nurse course.

UNDERSTAND HOW LIFE FACTORS AND EVENTS MAY INFLUENCE THE DEVELOPMENT OF THE INDIVIDUAL

ACTIVITY 9

INFLUENCES OF NATURE AND NURTURE

How influential has society and the environment been on your development?

Has the theory of nurturing had more influence on your life than the theory of the nativists?

Have you ever been told 'you have your mother's hair'? Or that you must have to work hard to have a figure like that!

Design a table with three columns – you might use the one beneath or design your own. Consider your physical attributes and the influences on your upbringing, list them in two columns, Nature or Nurture.

Do you require a fourth column, headed interaction?

Example:

Characteristic	Nature	Nurture
Eye colour	Brown from Grandma	
Weight	Overweight from Mother	Overweight, overeat, poor diet, little exercise!
Temperament		

This exercise is not as easy as it first appears!

Return to Activity 3.

Consider the factors that you have included in your lifeline, insert as many of these into the table as you can.

When you have completed the table, write a short article that demonstrates your understanding of the nature-nurture debate, include examples from your table to highlight the points you make.

ACTIVITY 10

NATURE-NURTURE

While it is now accepted that the two influences – nature (biology) and nurture (environment) – interact with each other and are virtually inseparable (Interactionism), there are researchers who investigate the relative contributions of nature and nurture factors in psychology and development.

The basic question is:

Are certain aspects of our behaviour, inclinations and perception determined at birth or do we have to learn them?

Devise a table that compares and contrasts the development of the individual from the perspectives of nature and nurture. (You might like to devise your own, or use the one below.)

You should consider the following areas of development:

- Language acquisition
- Causes of behaviour
- Gender role behaviour
- Aggression
- Perception

Include examples that support the theory and names of the theorists who propound and support the theory.

	Nature – determined at birth	Nurture – learnt
Language acquisition		
Causes of behaviour		
Gender role behaviour		
Aggression - example	Lorenz said aggression is innate and is an adaptive response, the strongest most aggressive control food, territory etc and so survive.	Bandura – the Bobo doll experiment, social learning of aggression. (You should investigate this experiment).
Perception		

LANGUAGE DEVELOPMENT: NATURE OR NURTURE?

Language development provides good examples of the differences of areas of research, and also of the interaction between genetically guided development and the contributions of experience and the environment.

Noam Chomsky and Burrhus Skinner both investigated language development, but their explanations were very different.

In pairs, research the work of Chomsky and Skinner.

Write an article that examines their investigations. Consider the following points:

■ the key elements of their research
■ the evidence that supports their work

When you have finished your articles, **as a class** compare and contrast your findings.

Devise a presentation that puts forward your results.

nb Chomsky – language innate; Skinner – language learnt.

FACTORS THAT MIGHT INFLUENCE DEVELOPMENT OF THE INDIVIDUAL

Many factors and events can influence the development of the individual; you are probably aware of the detrimental effect that smoking and alcohol both can have on the development of the individual. Other causes of impaired development will be new to you. In this and the next few activities, you will investigate some of these factors and events.

Using a table similar to the one below, put the following factors or events into the correct column:

Factor or event:

Bullying	Access to employment and income	Infections during pregnancy	Sickle cell anaemia
Down's syndrome	Foetal alcohol syndrome	Access to health and social care services	Education
Stress	Exercise	Discrimination	Access to leisure/recreational facilities
Cystic fibrosis	Nutrition and dietary choices	Gender	Pollution
The family	Water and sanitation	Community	Peer groups
Social class	Values and attitudes	Income	Expenditure
Employment status	Housing	Media	Culture and belief
Substance abuse			

Genetic	Biological	Environmental	Socio-economic	Lifestyle

ACTIVITY 13

GENETIC FACTORS THAT MIGHT INFLUENCE DEVELOPMENT OF THE INDIVIDUAL

There are 4,000 known inherited diseases, each one caused by the disruption of the normal base sequence of a gene, a substitution, a deletion or an insertion.

In Britain, cystic fibrosis is the most common inherited or genetic disease. In tropical Africa and the Mediterranean countries, sickle cell anaemia commonly affects many people; the Ashkenasi Jews of East European origin are affected by Tay Sachs disease.

Other major genetic disorders include Phenylk etonuria, Muscular Dystrophy and Down's Syndrome.

In small groups, each person select one of the disorders from those above.

■ Research the disorders and the effects they can have on the individual.

■ Find out if it is possible to detect the possibility of the disorder occurring before conception, or if it can be detected before birth of the baby.

- Consider how the disorder might effect the development of the individual, investigate all aspects of life including; physical, social, intellectual and emotional.
- Produce your findings as a presentation to inform the rest of your group.

ACTIVITY 14

CASE STUDY – JORDAN

Lifestyle, the environment and socio-economic factors might be interrelated to influence development of the individual.

Read the following (stereotypical) case study.

Jordan is 15; he attends the nearby school where he is amongst the smallest in his class – smaller than most of the girls. Jordan's mother works long hours doing shifts in a nursing home. Jordan's father has been unemployed for eight months since the car manufacturing plant closed down. He has not had any offers of work and now spends most of his time in the local club or at the betting office; most of his money goes on beer and cigarettes.

Since his dad was laid off, Jordan's parents have been arguing and fighting more and more.

The family live on an estate which is well known to the police and social services department as requiring frequent intervention. When the estate was built 20 years ago, a stream was diverted to run through a grassy area, it was thought that it would provide a pleasant environment for children to play – unfortunately this has proved not to be the case, and at night the area is considered a 'no-go' area.

The living conditions in the family home have started to deteriorate since Jordan's dad has been out of work. His mother no longer spends much time or effort on the housework, the cold water tap in the kitchen leaks and the toilet keeps becoming blocked – no-one has got round to informing the council, so repairs are not carried out.

A parade of shops and a post office are at the centre of the estate. The shops do not remain open for long as the competition from the large shopping centres is too great. The post office will close in the next few months despite a petition from the residents.

A health centre has been proposed but there has never been enough council or government money for this provision.

To provide an income for himself, Jordan does a paper round and most of the money he earns is spent on his favourite (video/pc) games or on chips and crisps – Jordan seems to be permanently hungry!

Jordan's sister, Shelley, is 13. Shelley has recently started smoking and when she goes out with her friends at the weekends she has developed a taste for sweet alcoholic drinks – she thinks that her parents don't know about these things. Shelley would like to have been an athlete as she is very fast on the track, but apart from the small school sports field there are no nearby athletic facilities. Shelley was excluded from school for a short period last year – her classmates know that she should not be messed with!

Jordan and Shelley have a baby sister, aged three. Before the baby came, Jordan and Shelley used to get pocket money and have occasional holidays but these have all disappeared. Jordan and Shelley used to be very fond of their sister but now she seems to be always crying and looks dirty – they try to ignore her as much as they can.

Write an article that discusses:

- how lifestyle, the environment and socio-economic factors have influenced the lives of Jordan and his sisters.
- the possible implications of these factors and events on the development of Jordan and his sisters.

UNPREDICTABLE AND PREDICTABLE EVENTS

The case study involving Jordan and his family might have highlighted some major life events for you – for example, redundancy and the birth of a sibling. You might have also considered the possibility of other factors, eg abuse, divorce, employment, leaving home etc.

Some of these events are predictable and even planned, while others are unpredictable.

The effects that these events will have on development of the individual might depend on whether or not they are predicted.

Some of the major life events could be both predictable and unpredictable – for example, a pregnancy or bereavement.

In pairs write a script for a television series that describes the influences of events and factors on the lives of individuals.

Give details that show how the lives of the characters are affected.

Include as many as possible of the following factors/events:

- birth of a sibling
- starting school/nursery
- moving house
- employment
- redundancy
- serious injury
- leaving home
- marriage
- divorce
- parenthood
- retirement
- ageing
- bereavement
- abuse

UNDERSTAND PHYSICAL CHANGES AND PSYCHOLOGICAL PERSPECTIVES IN RELATION TO AGEING

ACTIVITY 16

AGEING

There are very few certainties in life but one is that we are all getting older and we will all die!

Perhaps that sounds a bit morbid to you – but it is a fact and it is something that has to be dealt with in one way or another. Either – it is a fact and is something that has to be dealt with in one way or another. Or – it is a fact it is something that has to be dealt with in one way or another.

With a friend, consider 'ageing', and make notes that detail how you view people at each decade of their life. Describe your perception of the physical, intellectual, social and emotional aspects of life, and give examples of either people you know or people you are aware of (media personalities etc).

89

You might use a table similar to the one below to get you started.

	Physical	Social	Intellectual	Emotional
Childhood				
Teens				
Twenties				
Thirties				
Forties				
Fifties				
Sixties				
Seventies				
Eighties				
Nineties				

ACTIVITY 17

THEORIES OF AGEING

Activity theory (Havighurst et al 1968) and Disengagement theory (Cumming and Henry 1961) debate whether it is normal, healthy or even necessary for older adults to remain active as long as possible, or whether the more typical and healthy pattern is to disengage and gradually turn inward.

Research these two theories, and write an article that compares the similarities and contrasts the differences. Give examples that demonstrate the points that are made. Write a conclusion showing why you think one theory is more influential than the other.

ACTIVITY 18

HORMONE CONTROL – PUBERTY

Would you believe that chemical substances produced (mainly) in the body's endocrine cells is responsible for many of our emotions, behaviours and our physical characteristics?

Hormones play a central role in growth and development throughout life, the pituitary gland secretes growth hormone from as early as ten weeks after conception! Of all the endocrine glands, the most critical is the pituitary gland which provides the trigger for a release of hormones from other glands.

Of course, the best-known influences of hormones occur during puberty, in most people this will be during the teenage years.

Copy the chart below which lists the major hormones involved in physical growth and development, and complete columns two and three.

Gland	Hormone(s) secreted	Aspects of growth influenced
Pituitary		
Thyroid		
Adrenal		
Testes (boys)		
Ovaries (girls)		

ACTIVITY 19

HORMONE CONTROL – PUBERTY (CONT)

The hormone changes of puberty start the development of full sexual maturity.

In small groups, research the changes in both the primary and the secondary sex characteristics in boys and in girls.

Devise a set of illustrated posters informing the rest of the class of your findings, to be displayed in the classroom.

You might find the following website useful:

http://www.bbc.co.uk/science/humanbody/body/interactives/lifecycle/teenagers/

ACTIVITY 20

HORMONE CONTROL – MENOPAUSE

One of the landmarks of ageing for women is the menopause, which literally means the cessation of the menses (menarche/periods). Oestrogen levels begin to fluctuate and decline – there is not a similar physiological occurrence in men.

In addition to physical changes, it has been part of our folklore that the menopause causes major emotional upheaval.

Investigate the physiological effects and the possible psychological effects of the reduction of oestrogen during and after the menopause.

Keep a careful record of your research and reading in order that you can write a bibliography and reference any work that you quote from.

Write an article – it might be for a popular women's magazine – that discusses the menopause, any problems associated with it, and the myths that are attached to it.

ACTIVITY 21

PHYSICAL CHANGES AND AGEING

When does old age commence? The answer to this will depend on the age of the person asked – for example, a child of ten might think that someone of twenty is very old!

From one aspect the child is correct; from the mid-twenties onward a gradual decline takes place in both physical and psychological processes.

91

Working in small groups of three or four:

a) Devise a questionnaire that will enable you to write a report on the physical changes of the body in relation to the ageing process.

b) Include all systems of the body:

   i. Cardiovascular

   ii. Respiratory

   iii. Nervous

   iv. Musculo-skeletal

   v. Skin

c) Investigate the illnesses that are more likely to occur as a result of ageing.

d) Interview people of different ages in your work placement.

e) Tabulate the findings from your questionnaire, you might use the table below or one of your own design.

f) When you have completed points a)–e), write a report on the physical aspects of ageing and the diseases and disorders related to ageing.

System and age-related disorders	Cardiovascular	Respiratory	Nervous	Musculo-sketal	Skin	Age-Related illness
Twenties						
Thirties						
Forties						
Fifties						
Sixties						
Seventies						
Eighties						
Nineties						

ACTIVITY 22

PSYCHOLOGICAL ASPECTS OF AGEING

As you saw in the previous activity, there are many changes that occur throughout life. Some might be seen as positive, eg the deepening of the voice as the larynx becomes larger; some might be seen as negative, eg the appearance of 'liver spots' on the skin.

How these age-related changes are approached will depend on the character and personality of each individual.

Think of people you know (or people you might be aware of, eg TV characters) in three different decades, eg thirties, fifties, eighties; investigate the confidence (self-assurance) and self-esteem (self-respect) that they display.

With the knowledge you have gained, devise a series of stereotypical characters that could become part of a learning pack for carers in a social care setting.

ACTIVITY 23

POSITIVE AND NEGATIVE PERSPECTIVES

In pairs, write a 'script' that highlights both the positive and the negative effects of retirement and should also include cultural variations.

The characters will address the following points:

- Retirement, enforced or voluntary?
- Gender role changes
- Loss of a partner
- Loss of peers
- Learning for pleasure
- Leisure pursuits
- Finance – this could be negative, eg loss of income, or positive, eg maturing of investments
- Ageism

The script might also consider the need for admission to a care home and the likelihood of separation of a couple.

ANSWERS

ACTIVITY 6

Week 13   The foetus resembles a miniature human being and is about as heavy as a 50p coin. Nipples appear and a uterus, cervix and vagina form. If the baby is a boy, a penis is visible. Even as early as 13 weeks, the baby may find and suck her/his thumb.

Week 14   The eyebrows and lashes are starting to grow, the eyes have moved from the sides to the front of the head, and the ears have moved up from the neck to the head. The intestines are developing folds to absorb nutrients more efficiently.

Week 15   The heartbeat is strong and the body is growing fast to catch up with the well-developed head. Eyes are still tightly closed beneath sealed eyelids and the foetus is making 'rooting' movements ready to search for milk after birth.

Week 16   The bones are hardening and tiny nails appear. Blood vessels show through the translucent skin, which is now covered in fine, downy hair called lanugo. By now, the foetus weighs about the same as a small pot of yoghurt.

Week 17   With plenty of room to kick and roll around, the baby is very active. She/he's starting to lay down 'brown fat' around the kidneys, chest and the back of the neck, to help regulate temperature in the first weeks after the birth.

Week 18   The foetus has a big forehead and the eyes are sensitive to light. Hearing is sufficiently good for her/him to respond to loud noises and the mother's heartbeat can be heard.

Week 19   Permanent teeth are already forming buds behind the milkteeth buds in the jaw. The arms and legs are now in the same proportions that they'll be at birth. As the nerves and muscles develop the foetus can control her/his movements, and may bend the elbow or frown.

Week 20   The skin is starting to thicken into four layers and a creamy, moisturising substance called vernix covers it. She/he measures about 25cm from top to bottom.

Week 21   Antibodies are being transferred from the mother's blood to the foetus, to protect from infection during the early months of life. Taste buds are forming on the tongue, and water and sugars can be absorbed from the amniotic fluid.

Week 22   The foetus can look from side to side, hear loud music or shouting, and distinguish sweet tastes from bitter ones. If she/he starts doing acrobatics just as the mother is dropping off to sleep, it could be because when resting she breathes more deeply, with the result that the oxygen supply to the foetus increases.

Week 23   The foetus looks very much how she/he will when born – although the skin is quite red and wrinkled, and more fat stores will be laid down over the next few weeks. There are even has lines on the fingers - fingerprints!

Week 24   Vital organs are now mature but the lungs aren't ready to cope with independent breathing. If labour started now special care would be required. Any baby born at or after this time is considered 'viable' because it has a chance of surviving.

Week 25   She/he may suck her/his thumb, and already has a preference for using the right or left hand. She/he can hear and might even recognise the mother's voice.

Week 26   She/he is becoming plumper so the skin, which is gradually thickening, looks smoother and more opaque. Eyelashes are formed and the eyes will open this week. Virtually all babies are born with blue or dark blue eyes and it's not until some weeks after birth that they become the colour they'll stay.

Week 27   The heart rate is around 120 to 160 beats per minute, roughly twice the speed of yours. If born prematurely there would be a fair chance of survival, although problems with breathing and keeping warm would mean special care would be required.

Week 28   Airways are developing and the foetus is moving regularly. Babies kick most vigorously before week 30, after which space becomes more restricted, and all this activity helps their muscles develop.

Week 29   The brain is bigger and amazingly complex, the lungs are maturing in preparation for the first breath and the irises are starting to dilate.

Week 30   The body is about 33cm long from head to bottom. The amniotic fluid cushions and protects the foetus against Braxton Hicks Contractions.

Week 31   She/he's still laying down fat stores and will almost double in weight before birth. The creamy moisturiser and fine, downy hair on the body are beginning to disappear and the lungs are producing surfactant, a substance that will help them to inflate more easily after birth.

Week 32   She/he has rapid eye movements during sleep, just like you when you're dreaming. She measures around 40.5cm from head to bottom, but if she were born now she'd still need special care.

Week 33   She/he's probably settled into the birth position and the midwife can tell you which way she/he's going to be born. Head downwards is the norm, but some babies remain in a breech position and a few lie across the uterus.

Week 34   Fluid is passing through the foetus's kidneys and is recycled back into the amniotic fluid. She/he's drawing on the mother's calcium reserves to harden her bones, so she needs to eat plenty of calcium-rich foods.

Week 35   She/he's going through a rapid growth phase and may gain up to 227g ($\frac{1}{2}$lb) a week. Through the wall of the mother's stomach the open eyes can differentiate between darkness and light.

Week 36   The hearing is increasingly acute, the nails are growing and she/he may be born with a full head of hair. She/he weighs about 5$\frac{1}{2}$lb (2.5kg) and measures 46cm from head to bottom.

Week 37   The finger and toenails are now complete, which means that she/he is considered clinically mature, though she/he'll continue to gain about 28g a day. A boy's testicles will have descended from his abdomen into his scrotum.

Week 38   Growth slows down in the last week or two.

Week 39   Some antibodies are passing from the mother through the placenta into the bloodstream to give the immune system a boost for the first six months while it matures. The bowel contains meconium – a sticky, tar-like substance that will be excreted as the first poo soon after birth.

Week 40   She/he's plump, mature and finally ready for life outside the uterus. She/he's roughly 51cm long, though of course newborn babies vary greatly in size and weight.

ACTIVITY 18

HORMONES

Gland	Hormone(s) secreted	Aspects of growth influenced
Pituitary	Growth hormone, activating hormones	Rate of physical maturation. Signals other glands to secrete hormones
Thyroid	Thyroxine	Normal brain development and overall rate of growth
Adrenal	Adrenal androgen	Some changes at puberty, specifically the development of secondary sex characteristics in girls

Gland	Hormone(s) secreted	Aspects of growth influenced
Testes (boys)	Testosterone	Formation of male genitals prenatally. Triggers the sequence of primary and secondary sex characteristic changes at puberty in males.
Ovaries (girls)	Oestrogen	Development of the menstrual cycle and breasts in girls.

UNIT 5 – FUNDAMENTALS OF ANATOMY AND PHYSIOLOGY FOR HEALTH AND SOCIAL CARE

This section focuses on: P1, P2, P3, P4, P5, P6, M1, M2, M3, D1, D2.

Introduction and Learning Outcomes

This unit introduces the student to the human body, from the cellular structure and function to detailed knowledge of the anatomy and physiology of the systems.

Energy metabolism and homeostatic mechanisms will be investigated and related health and social care.

1 Understand the organisation of the human body.

2 Understand the functioning of the body systems associated with energy metabolism.

3 Understand how homeostatic mechanisms operate in the maintenance of an internal environment.

4 Be able to interpret data obtained from monitoring routine variations in the functioning of healthy body systems.

Content

1) Understand the organisation of the human body

Organisation; Cells; Tissues; Body organs; Systems; Main functions of systems.

2) Understand the functioning of the body systems associated with energy and metabolism

Energy laws; Forms of energy; Energy metabolism; cardiovascular system; Respiratory system; Digestive system; Role of enzymes in digestion; Major products of digestion; Absorption of food.

3) Understand how homeostatic mechanisms operate in the maintenance of an internal environment

Homeostasis; homeostatic mechanisms for regulation.

4) Be able to interpret data obtained from monitoring routine variations in the functioning of healthy body systems

Measurements; Normal variations; Data presentation and interpretation.

Grading criteria

P1 Describe the functions of the main cell components

P2 Describe the structure of the main tissues of the body and their role in the functioning of two named body organs

P3 Describe the gross structure and main functions of all major body systems

P4 Describe the role of energy in the body and the physiology of three named body systems in relation to energy metabolism

Describe the function of power in the body and how three named body systems work to produce energy from food.

P5 Describe the concept of homeostasis and the homeostatic mechanisms that regulate heart rate, breathing rate, body temperature and blood glucose levels

P6 Measure body temperature, heart rate and breathing rate before and after a standard period of exercise, interpret the data and comment on its validity

M1 Explain the physiology of three named body systems in relation to energy metabolism

Explain how three named body systems work to convert food to heat, work or electrical energy.

M2 Explain the probable homeostatic responses to changes in the internal environment during exercise

To meet M2 you should be able to explain what happens in the cell to ensure that a stable environment is maintained following exercise in which body temperature, heart and respiration rates increase.

M3 Analyse data obtained to show how homeostatic mechanisms control the internal environment during exercise.

To meet M3, evaluate the information you have gathered from P6 to show that temperature, heart and breathing rates increase during exercise.

D1 Use examples to explain how body systems interrelate with each other

Although body systems can be investigated independently, they must work together in order to function efficiently. For example, the respiratory and cardio-vascular systems could be examined jointly to explain the maintenance of oxygen provision to the cells, and removal of carbon dioxide.

D2 Explain the importance of homeostasis in maintaining the healthy functioning of the body

To meet D2 you should explain why a stable environment is necessary for a healthy body.

UNDERSTAND THE ORGANISATION OF THE HUMAN BODY

ACTIVITY 1

ORGANISATION

The human body is complex in its order and organisation. The organisation of the body can be considered by levels, starting with the simple, proceeding to the most complex.

Below are descriptions. Link the noun to the description; put them in order of hierarchy – simplest to most complex.

Nouns – organs; cells; systems; tissues.

Descriptions:

- A group of cells with similar structure and function. Classified into four types: epithelial, connective, muscle, nervous.
- A group of organs classified as a unit because of a common function or set of functions. The body is considered to have 11 major groups.
- Basic living units of all plants and animals. Although the types differ in structure and function they have many characteristics in common.
- Composed of two or more tissue types that perform one or more common functions.

ACTIVITY 2

THE CELL

In order to understand how the cell works, it is necessary to understand the basic anatomy. Cells change as they develop; their structure changes to allow them to fulfil special functions.

(It is not necessary to have a detailed understanding of cell microstructure and metabolism; an overview is all that is required.)

Find a diagram of the structure of a basic animal cell, copy the diagram and label the following structures:

- Cell membrane
- Nucleus
- Cytoplasm
- Organelles –
    Mitochondria
    Endoplasmic reticulum (smooth and rough)
    Golgi apparatus
    Lysosome

ACTIVITY 3

TISSUES

Work in pairs to prepare a leaflet that could be referred to by other students.

a) Using a microscope and prepared histology slides, draw tissue from each of the following tissue types:

- Epithelial: simple (cuboidal, columnar, squamous, ciliated), compound (simple, keratinised)

- Connective: blood, cartilage, bone, areolar, adipose
- Muscle: striated, non striated, cardiac
- Nervous: neurones, neuroglia

b) For each of the types of tissue that you have drawn, write a short paragraph that describes its role in the function of its organ or body part.

c) Link your diagrams to pictures that indicate the location of the tissue.

ACTIVITY 4

BODY ORGANS

Draw large diagrams of the human body, the male and female, to be displayed in the classroom. Locate the following organs:

Heart – lungs – brain – stomach – liver – pancreas – duodenum – ileum – colon – kidneys – bladder – ovaries – testes – uterus

To assist you in this activity go to the following website and play the interactive 'organs' game. http://www.bbc.co.uk/science/humanbody/body/

ACTIVITY 5

SKIN FUNCTION

The skin is part of the integumentary system, as are the nails, hair and the sweat, oil and wax glands.

The diagram below outlines the structure and some of the many functions of the skin.

Design an illustrated talk to present to your colleagues that will demonstrate your understanding of the structure and functions of the skin.

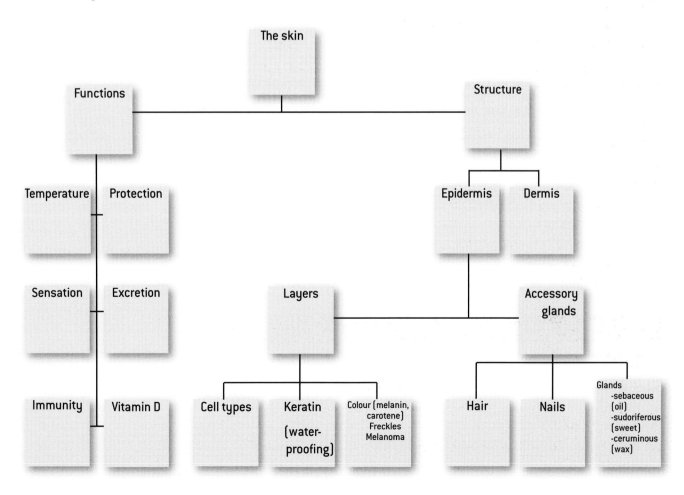

99

ACTIVITY 6

STRUCTURES AND FUNCTIONS

In this section you will investigate the gross structure (large structures) and main function of the systems of the body.

Work in small groups to produce a learning pack that would be suitable for use by cadet nurses.

- Include large, clearly labelled diagrams of each system and its location in the body.
- Give clear descriptions of the function of each system.
- An overview of the interactions of the different structures within each system should be included.
- Tables, flow charts or other illustrations should be incorporated to clarify descriptions if appropriate.

Include the following:

System	Function
Cardiovascular	Transport and supply of materials to cells
Respiratory	Maintenance of oxygen supply
Digestive	Digestion of food materials
Renal	Elimination of waste products
Nervous	Receives information from the environment. Co-ordinates with the endocrine system to regulate body activities
Endocrine	Produces hormones, regulates reproductive function
Reproductive	Reproduction
Lymphatic	Transports fluid (lymph) from tissues to the blood. Also functions as part of the body's defence mechanism
Musculo-skeletal	To produce movement, protect the organs of the body, provide a framework, produce cells and heat, to store energy etc.
Immune	The skin, defensive cells, chemicals, lymphatic system

UNDERSTAND THE FUNCTIONING OF THE BODY SYSTEMS ASSOCIATED WITH ENERGY AND METABOLISM

ACTIVITY 7

ENERGY LAWS – SUPPLYING ENERGY TO THE CELLS OF THE BODY

The law of conservation of energy states that:

Energy can neither be created nor destroyed, only changed from one form to another.

Your body is like a machine – it requires energy to function. Energy can be defined as the capacity to do work.

The energy that your body uses comes from the food you eat, but metabolism (chemical processes) must occur before the energy can be released.

Research the questions below and write short answers:

- How does the food you eat become the energy that enables you to function?
- Describe the process of metabolism.
- What does your body do so that you can use the energy to perform? To grow? To repair?

Ensure that you include in your discussion; anabolism, catabolism, adenosine triphosphate (ATP), adenosine diphosphate (ADP), dehydration synthesis, hydrolysis, cellular respiration.

ACTIVITY 8

ENERGY METABOLISM

Read the following statements carefully:

- The human ear serves as a transducer, converting sound energy to mechanical energy.
- Light energy is converted in the eye to electrical energy.
- Heat energy and metabolism are related.
- During the breakdown of food molecules, chemical reactions take place that are the source of chemical energy.
- Electrical energy plays an important part in the transmission of messages.

Using diagrams where appropriate, write detailed explanations of the statements above.

ACTIVITY 9

ENERGY METABOLISM

The basal metabolic rate (BMR) is the amount of energy that is necessary to maintain life and to keep the body functioning at a minimal level.

The cardiovascular system, respiratory system and digestive system all play a part in ensuring that the body has the necessary energy.

Investigate the role that each of the three systems plays in supplying energy to the cells of the body to ensure a satisfactory BMR.

Devise a poster that explains your findings, to be displayed in the classroom.

ACTIVITY 10

FUNCTIONING OF BODY SYSTEMS

The class is divided into three groups, each group to take one of the following systems:

- Cardiovascular system, to include heart, cardiac cycle, heart rate, stroke volume, blood pressure, blood vessels – arteries, arterioles, capillaries, venules, veins; pulmonary and systemic circulations and the structure and functions of blood.

- Respiratory system, to include role of air passages in nose; structure and functions of trachea, bronchi, lungs – bronchial tree, alveoli; ciliated epithelial tissue, respiratory muscles – intercostals muscles, diaphragm; ventilation, gaseous exchange, diffusion.

- Digestive system, to include alimentary canal – oesophagus, stomach, duodenum, ileum, colon; liver, pancreas, salivary glands; role of digestive system in breakdown and absorption of food materials – ingestion, peristalsis, digestion, absorption, egestion.

Devise an interactive game that will assist students learning about the structure and function of the systems, and the roles that the relevant organs and tissues play.

The game might be influenced by online games, board games, or construction games etc.

Look at the following website for ideas:

http://www.bbc.co.uk/science/humanbody/body/

ACTIVITY 11

CHEMICAL DIGESTION

Amylases, proteases and lipases are enzymes that act on nutrients to speed up hydrolysis (a slow process using water to split molecules). Enzymes do not alter the reactions, just make them occur more rapidly.

Devise a table that illustrates which enzyme acts upon which nutrient, the action that takes place and the source of the action.

Ensure that you include all of the following:

Amylases, proteases, lipases, salivary glands, pancreas, stomach, small intestine.

Example of table:

Enzyme	Source	Action

ACTIVITY 12

MAJOR PRODUCTS OF DIGESTION

The major products of digestion are peptides and amino acids; sugars; glycerol and fatty acids. What happens to these nutrients when they reach this molecular state?

This activity will help you understand how the nutrients are metabolised to give necessary energy to the body.

There are two major metabolic states in the body, the absorptive state, which occurs immediately after a meal; and the postabsorptive state, which occurs after each absorptive state is concluded.

Research these two metabolic states; write your findings on large posters to inform the rest of your group.

You should include:

- detail of absorption of food into blood and lacteals
- the role of villi and microvilli
- storage of fats and carbohydrates.

Take the project further by considering:

- protein metabolism – and deamination of excess proteins
- the role of the liver
- the role of the kidneys
- fate of the end products.

You might wish to illustrate your posters with diagrams, pictures or flowcharts.

UNDERSTAND HOW HOMEOSTATIC MECHANISMS OPERATE IN THE MAINTENANCE OF AN INTERNAL ENVIRONMENT

ACTIVITY 13

HOMEOSTASIS

Homeostatic mechanisms are the processes by which the body maintains homeostasis – a stable environment in which cells can function. The internal environment refers to the tissue fluid that surrounds and bathes every cell of the body. Conditions must remain constant; a slight change in the cell environment can slow or stop a vital chemical reaction, leading to illness or even death.

The chemical content, temperature and pressure must all remain the same – homeostasis.

A 'negative feedback' mechanism works to bring disrupted homeostatic balance back to normal.

You can find many diagrams explaining negative feedback. Using these to help you, design a large flowchart related to a specific body system that demonstrates the working of a negative feedback mechanism.

ACTIVITY 14

HOMEOSTASIS AND THE HEALTHY BODY

Keith is to go into hospital to have surgery on his thyroid gland.

The doctors have told Keith that only part of the thyroid gland will be removed. It is essential that some thyroid tissue is left in place. In the past, total removal of the thyroid gland sometimes resulted in tetany and death.

Using your knowledge of the homeostatic mechanism, write a detailed article explaining the reasons why Keith will only have a partial removal of his thyroid gland.

(Tetany: severe muscle spasm – spasm of the respiratory muscles could be fatal.)

ACTIVITY 15

HOMEOSTATIC MECHANISMS

The nervous and endocrine systems work together to control homeostasis, but all organ systems help to maintain normal conditions of the internal environment.

Homeostatic mechanisms are used for the regulation of:

- heart rate
- breathing rate
- body temperature
- blood glucose levels.

Work in a group of four, with each person selecting one of the above areas.

Investigate these areas in depth. Devise a presentation to demonstrate the action of the mechanism at work in the body.

Support your presentation with an information pack that can be used as an aid to learning.

Ensure that the following are included in your research:

- Heart rate: roles of internal receptors, autonomic nervous system – sympathetic and parasympathetic nerve supply, cardiac centre, sinoatrial node; effects of increased body temperature and adrenaline on heart rate
- Breathing rate: roles of internal receptors, autonomic nervous system – sympathetic and parasympathetic nerve supply, respiratory centre, diaphragm and intercostal muscles
- Body temperature: production of heat by the body, eg through metabolic processes; loss of heat by the body – radiation, conduction, convection, evaporation; roles of hypothalamus, autonomic nervous system – sympathetic and parasympathetic nerve supply, skin – role of arterioles and sweat glands; effects of shivering; implications of surface area to volume ratios – eg in the care of babies; fever
- Blood glucose levels: roles of pancreas, liver, insulin, glucagon

BE ABLE TO INTERPRET DATA OBTAINED FROM MONITORING ROUTINE VARIATIONS IN THE FUNCTIONING OF HEALTHY BODY SYSTEMS

ACTIVITY 16

MEASUREMENTS – TEMPERATURE

Core temperature is the temperature measured around the internal organs. The average core temperature is 37.6°C.

Working in pairs, measure your own and your partner's body temperature, both before and after vigorous activity.

Record the findings on a graph. (It is normal to wait at least 1 hour after vigorous exercise or a hot bath before measuring body temperature, and to wait for 20 to 30 minutes after smoking, eating, or drinking a hot or cold liquid.)

Electronic thermometers are most commonly used and recommended. The temperature is displayed on a digital readout. Follow the directions that come with the thermometer. Electronic ear thermometers are common and convenient.

Following the activity, write a paragraph to show how homeostatic mechanisms control the internal environment when additional heat is needed to maintain core temperature.

ACTIVITY 17

MEASUREMENTS – PULSE AND RESPIRATION

The efficiency of the cardiovascular and respiratory systems can indicate an individual's general health. They can be monitored simply using non-invasive procedures.

Working in pairs, measure your own and your partner's pulse and respiration rates: when you have been resting; after gentle exercise; and after vigorous exercise, eg Harvard Step Test – instructions below.

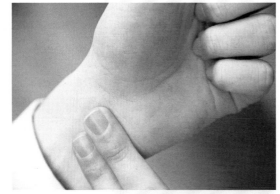

Following vigorous exercise, measure the pulse rate every two minutes until it has returned to the resting rate.

At the same time, measure the respiration rate. Try to do this unobtrusively. Count the number of respirations by observing the chest rising. Do this unobtrusively, again for 15 or 20 seconds and multiply to obtain the number of respirations per minute.

Record all the results on a chart. Draw a graph showing the pulse rates against time, and another graph to show the respiration rates against time.

Write a short paragraph that explains the results.

Measuring the pulse rate is a simple technique. Using either two fingers on the radial artery where it crosses the wrist, or a pulse meter, measure the rate for either 15 or 20 seconds, multiply by the appropriate number (four or three) to arrive at the number of beats per minute.

Harvard Step Test

The purpose of the Harvard Step Test is to determine aerobic fitness using a simple test and minimal equipment. For this activity only a shortened version is used, omitting the calculations, as a measurement of Fitness Index is not required.

Using a 50.8cm (20") platform and a stopwatch, step up and down on the platform at a rate of 30 steps per minute (every two seconds) for five minutes or until exhaustion. Exhaustion is defined as when the stepping rate stops for 15 seconds. On completion of the test immediately sit down.

The total number of heartbeats is counted between 1 to 1½ minutes after finishing.

ACTIVITY 18

HOMEOSTATIC MECHANISMS

Using the information obtained in Activity 17, analyse the data to show how homeostatic mechanisms control the internal environment during exercise and write a paragraph that demonstrates your understanding.

ACTIVITY 19

SAFE PRACTICES

It used to be normal practice to take the body temperature using a glass mercury thermometer.

Develop a leaflet that explains the safe practices that should be used when taking temperature, pulse and respiration measurements.

ANSWERS

ACTIVITY 1

ORGANISATION

Correct order:

Noun	Description
Cells	Basic living units of all plants and animals. Although the types differ in structure and function they have many characteristics in common
Tissues	A group of cells with similar structure and function. Classified into four types: epithelial, connective, muscle, nervous
Organs	Composed of two or more tissue types that perform one or more common functions
Systems	A group of organs classified as a unit because of a common function or set of functions. The body is considered to have 11 major groups

MARKED ASSIGNMENTS

Unit 1: Developing Effective Communication in Health and Social Care

SAMPLE ASSIGNMENT

This assignment meets the following Learning outcomes and Grading criteria:

LO 2 – Understand factors that influence communication and interpersonal interactions in health and social care setting

LO 3 – Know how patients/service users may be assisted by effective communication

P3 – Describe factors that may influence communication and interpersonal interactions with particular reference to health and social care settings

P4 – Identify how the communication needs of patients/service users may be assisted, including non-verbal communication

M2 – Explain the specific communication needs patients/service users may have that require support, including the use of technology

D1 – Analyse how communication in health and social care settings assists patients/service users and other key people

Scenario

As a worker in the health and social care profession it will be essential that you have good communication skills and can understand the challenges that others have to face in order to communicate effectively.

A new residential and nursing home will be opening in your neighbourhood and you have been offered a position in the team of care workers.

During your induction week – and before the tenants take up residence, staff have been allocated a variety of tasks to help ensure that residents are happy and comfortable in their new home.

Tasks

1 You have been asked to devise an information document that informs **ALL** staff of issues that might influence the way in which they communicate and relate to residents and to each other. **(P3)**

2 As the service users will have a variety of communication needs, many different approaches must be considered to ensure effective understanding. You have also been asked to devise a detailed chart for display in the staff office that identifies how communication needs may be addressed. You might use pictures to help explain your information.

The chart should be accompanied by a written report that explains each of the needs and details the type of support that can be given in each case. **(P4, M2)**

3 When attending your induction week at the residential nursing home you became aware of the large number of visitors, friends and relatives, and staff from a variety of professions that would be employed or visiting the home to meet service users and other staff.

Investigate the ways in which communication might support the interactions that will be taking place between all these individuals and compile an analysis of your findings. **(D1)**

PASS LEVEL ANSWER

UNIT 1: DEVELOPING EFFECTIVE COMMUNICATION IN HEALTH AND SOCIAL CARE
ASSIGNMENT – by Briony Hale
Task 1.

INFORMATION SHEET FOR ALL STAFF

It does not matter who you are!

When you talk to service users you must use interpersonal skills:

- Be polite
- Be respectful
- Think about what you want to say before you say it
- Do not gossip, be aware of confidentiality
- Keep information private, be aware of data protection

In addition to interpersonal skills other factors include

- Barriers that should be overcome
- Environment, noise, temperature
- If English is not the first language, translator or interpreters could be used
- For those with impaired hearing or speech problems, sign language or Makaton can be used.

Influences on communication in health and social care

- Be aware of your non-verbal communications
- Use eye contact, gestures and facial expressions
- Encourage responses by prompting and ensuring that you have understood accurately
- Do not push residents into situations e.g. if someone is shy they might be uncomfortable mixing with others in groups.
- Be aware of cultural or religious requirements, e.g. not shaking hands, or making eye contact with some groups

111

Task 2

Communication Need	Assistance
Hard of hearing	Hearing aid – might need assistance putting it in – ensure batteries are not flat
English not first language	Might need translator, notices in other languages
Poor vision	Use of Braille
Poor reading skills	Use of pictures, images
Shy, difficulty in relating to others	Support workers

ASSESSOR FEEDBACK FORM

UNIT 1: DEVELOPING EFFECTIVE COMMUNICATION IN HEALTH AND SOCIAL CARE ASSIGNMENT – PASS LEVEL ANSWER

P3 – The information document that you have devised, Briony, illustrates factors that might influence communication and interpersonal interactions in the health/social care setting. I would like to have seen some more detailed information but you have met the criteria.

P4 NOT MET – Briony, in this case a picture does not speak a thousand words! You have devised a chart; unfortunately you have not included detail as required by the assessment criteria, so you have not achieved P4 yet.

To achieve P4 you should include a written report that explains the specific communication needs that require support. Identify the needs of the service users/patients; link these needs to the type of support that would be beneficial. The support might be technical or interpersonal; review your lesson notes carefully before you resubmit the assignment.

M2 – Not attempted

D1 – Not attempted

MERIT LEVEL ANSWER

UNIT 1: DEVELOPING EFFECTIVE COMMUNICATION IN HEALTH AND SOCIAL CARE
ASSIGNMENT – by Mo Azir
Task 1.

An information document that informs all staff of issues that might influence the way in which they communicate and relate to residents and each other.

For All Staff.

Please read this leaflet carefully, it will help you identify factors that can help in your everyday work.

1. Barriers – be aware of factors that hinder communication, uncomfortable seating, temperature too high or too low.
2. Language – do you say what you mean? ensure you speak clearly and use jargon free language
3. Attitude – and behaviour, do not bring problems to work. Understand how your temperament can affect your communication and be perceived by others e.g. aggression
4. Preferred language – the first language might not be spoken. If there are sensory impairments Basic Sign Language, Makaton or Braille might be preferred
5. Images – signs, diagrams, pictures all can influence interactions.
6. Technology – hearing aids with efficient batteries, speech aids, mobile phones, texting
7. Interpersonal skills – trust, respect, maintaining confidentiality
8. Supporting – therapists, advocates, interpreters,
9. Personality – shy, lonely, putting service users into group activities might be insensitive if they are not used to this sort of thing.

Task 2

A chart that identifies how communication needs of service users might be assisted.

Communication Need	Assistance
Hearing or speech impairment	Lip reading, hearing aid, basic sign language, Makaton, speech machines
English not first language	Interpreters, translator
Learning disabilities	Personal communication passports
Acute illness	Speech therapist, psychologist
New staff	Staff training
New service users	Learning to trust, respect,
Unable to hear/speak on phone	Mobile phone, texting

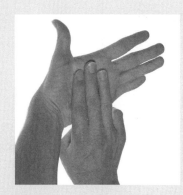  

Report that explains specific communication needs that service users/patients may have that require support.

For those with impaired hearing – Impaired hearing can range from no hearing at all to a slight hearing loss. Staff should be aware that some people with hearing difficulties will not use hearing aids. Staff should face the individual directly, speak clearly and precisely but not shouting. Care should be taken not frighten individuals by appearing to 'creep up' on them.

Service users that use hearing aids should have batteries replaced regularly.

Others with hearing impairments might use basic sign language or Makaton.

Other technology can be used to assist those with speech difficulties e.g. speech devices and texting on mobile phones – text messages can also be sent to landlines. Computers can be used, e.g. email, chat rooms etc

Staff training is important and all new staff should be introduced to policies of data protection and equal rights etc. Personal Communication Passports should be introduced to staff.

For those whose first language is different, interpreters or translators may be required. Before organizing translators for the service user/patient, the worker should find out if that is what is required. If the service user has been in England speaking English for many years no service might be required.

A service user or patient who has had a stroke or other acute illness might benefit from speech therapy or other therapist.

ASSESSOR FEEDBACK FORM

UNIT 1: DEVELOPING EFFETIVE COMMUNICATION IN HEALTH AND SOCIAL CARE ASSIGNMENT – MERIT LEVEL ANSWER

P3 – Mo, you have met this criterion well. This is an interesting document that would be suitable for staff information. You have considered factors that would influence communication and interpersonal interactions with particular reference to health and social care settings.

P4 – This criterion has been met. You have devised a chart that could be displayed in the staff office; you have identified communication needs and linked them to specific methods of assistance.

M2 – You have explained specific communication needs for service users/patients that require support in some detail and have met this criterion. Mo, you have given good examples of the specific needs and illustrate your understanding clearly.

D1 – Not attempted. To meet this criterion you must analyse how communication can assist patients, service users and key people in health or social care settings.

DISTINCTION LEVEL ANSWER

UNIT 1: DEVELOPING EFFECTIVE COMMUNICATION IN HEALTH AND SOCIAL CARE
ASSIGNMENT – by Lizanne Shakespeare
Task 1

Issues that influence communication and interpersonal interactions, an information document for staff.

At some point in their life every one will come into a health or social care setting, whether as a young child, a sick adult, or an elderly person needing care. Personalities, cultures, technology, art and science all have a part to play in communication and interpersonal interactions.

In the health and social care sector communication is used to talk about needs, concerns, attitudes and feelings as well as to impart information. In order to ensure that all communication and interpersonal needs are met, this leaflet has been divided into sections, although some issues could appear in more than one section.

Communication and language needs and preferences

The most obvious difference in communication is a language, where possible interpreters, signers or technology will be used to enable a service user to practice their *preferred language*. It may be an advantage to include symbols or pictures when posting notices of information for service users, to ensure that they are clearly understood.

When communicating *face to face* with service users or colleagues staff must consider not only the words and expressions they use, but must also think about their body language, posture, gestures, facial expression and other aspects of *non-verbal communication* (NVC). It would be easy to give an impression of disinterest to a service user (or a colleague) by being distracted or appearing bored. By being attentive and using appropriate *paralanguage* – tone of voice, volume, pitch and speed of language, it is not difficult to encourage communication.

Staff should have good *listening skills*; communication is not just about hearing what is said, but understanding what the service user really means.

It is said that up to 80% of communication is non-verbal. *Sensory contact* plays an important part not only in listening, but in eye contact, touch and in spatial awareness (presence). Staff should be aware that not everyone is happy or comfortable to be touched or hugged.

Environment

Communication in the health and social care setting can also be influenced by the environment. For example, the work that happens every day in a ward

117

or nursing home can be *noisy* and certainly not conducive to disclosure of personal feelings e.g. vacuum cleaners, television, radio etc.

If a group meeting is taking place, there should be sufficient *seats* for all – of the correct type, it would not do for staff to drop off to sleep in arm chairs in the middle of important case conferences. The *temperature* of a room can have an effect on concentration; too hot and people become sleepy, too cold and they lose concentration.

Consideration should also be given to the setting for communication. While pulling screens around a bed might give visual *privacy*, it does not necessarily mean that no-one else can hear the conversation taking place.

Behaviour

Staff should be aware of *attitudes and behaviours*, not only in others but also in themselves. Interactions can have a negative or a positive effect on an individual's health and social well being. If a service user is pushed into activities or groups in which they are not happy their sense of *isolation* or loneliness can be compounded. Often service users feel *helpless* and exposed to the actions and opinions of others especially their carers, staff should be *responsive* to messages they receive and ensure that what might appear light-hearted or a joke to colleagues might appear rude and *insensitive* to patients/service users; what might seem as encouragement and persuasion might be perceived as *bullying* or harassment to others.

Barriers

Barriers to communication have been discussed briefly above, however there are many factors that influence communication and can prevent information being passed effectively.

Jargon and *complex language* can be confusing, not only to service users but also to colleagues and professionals in other agencies. *Disability* can be a major barrier to communication, but there are many methods of overcoming them including; *technological* aids e.g. hearing aids, speech devices etc; communication passports, *non-verbal languages* e.g. Makaton, Braille, Basic Sign Language etc.

Other barriers to communication have been touched on briefly throughout this task, but in the health and social care settings it would be impossible to cover every aspect. It should be remembered that as a worker in the health or social care setting a degree of power is held – and that can be abused.

Task 2

A chart to identify how communication needs might be assisted. A written report explaining the needs and detailing the type of support.

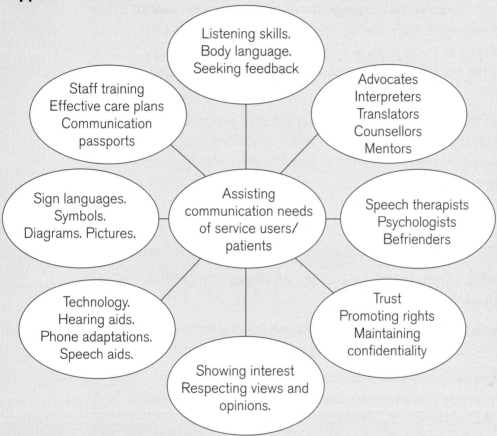

It can be seen from the diagram above that there are many ways in which communication needs could be addressed.

The type of support required will be determined by the need of the service user/patient, but one of the most important areas to consider is that of staff training and updating. Staff should also be aware of the significance of trust, promoting service user's rights and maintaining confidentiality (although staff should be aware that there are occasions when a confidence cannot and should not be kept). Demonstrating respect and valuing the views of others are important factors in developing self-esteem and encouraging positive self-image. Staff should ensure that these qualities are promoted.

Those with specific communication needs, hearing, speech or visual impairments, will have specific means of resolving their difficulties. They might be technological, and have instruction manuals that should be understood and implemented. There might be simple aids that must be maintained e.g. hearing aids requiring new batteries.

Good use should be made of diagrams, symbols etc that will address the needs of those whose first language is different. Non-verbal languages, Makaton, Basic Sign Language, Braille etc would be used by trained staff but can be learnt and used by all.

Personal Communication Passports are a practical and person-centred way of supporting children, young people and adults who cannot easily speak for themselves. They identify the user as a person, not a set of problems or difficulties to be dealt with. The use of these passports could be extended to many areas where communication needs require enhancement.

Additional communication needs can be met through support services. Liaising with professionals in other agencies to introduce befrienders, advocates or other personnel can identify areas of communication that have become a stumbling block.

Task 3

An analysis of how communication assists all those in health or social care settings

Without communication nothing would get done, no information would be passed on, in fact – the world would probably come to a stand still!

In the health and social care settings communication takes place not only between service users/patients and workers, but also between relatives, friends and workers from other agencies.

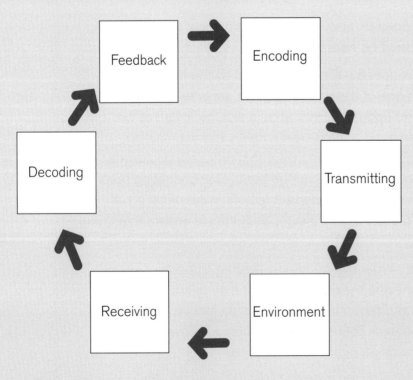

For successful communication to take place the chain of communication should be unbroken.

In order to analyse how communications in health and social care settings support service users/patients and other key users it is necessary to identify the many and varied interactions that take place.

Communications take place to inform, to support, educate, give and receive instruction, keep records, liaise and coordinate. All of these communications can assist any or all of the service users and key people in the health or social care settings.

Interactions occur from the moment that individuals become service users/patients until they die – and even then communications continue to assist relatives and key workers.

ASSESSOR FEEDBACK FORM

UNIT 1: DEVELOPING EFFECTIVE COMMUNICATION IN HEALTH AND SOCIAL CARE ASSIGNMENT – DISTINCTION LEVEL ANSWER

Lizanne, this is a good introduction to Task 1; you lead straight to the main points without waffling.

P3 – You have addressed this criterion by describing many factors that could influence communication and interpersonal interactions. You have avoided compiling a list but have carefully selected topics and discussed their relevance. By highlighting important points the leaflet would be easy to read and understand.

P4 – This chart would be valuable in a staff office. It clearly identifies skills and factors that can assist in communication needs of service users/patients.

M2 – Your written report explains the type of support that can be given to meet needs.

D1 – A difficult task that you have addressed well. You have included the communication cycle to demonstrate the importance of an unbroken chain, but not gone into detail as it was not required for this task; well done.

You could have included some specific examples giving evidence of communication assisting individuals, but these were not asked for.

Unit 3: Health, Safety and Security in Health and Social Care

SAMPLE ASSIGNMENT

This assignment meets the following Learning outcomes and Grading criteria:

LO 2 – Understand how legislation, guidelines, policies and procedures promote health, safety and security

LO 3 – Understand roles and responsibilities for health, safety and security in health and social care settings

LO 4 – Know how to deal with hazards in a local environment

P2 – Describe how key legislation in relation to health, safety and security influences health and social care delivery

P3 – Using examples from work experience describe how policies and procedures promote health, safety and security in the health and social care workplace

P4 – Examine the roles and responsibilities of key people in the promotion of health, safety and security in a health or social care setting

P5 – Carry out a health and safety survey of a local environment used by a specific patient/ service user group

M1 – Explain how legislation, policies and procedures are used to promote the health, safety and security of individuals in the health and social care workplace

M2 – Assess the risk associated with the use of the chosen local environment and make recommendations for change

D1 – Using examples from work experience evaluate the effectiveness of policies and procedures for promoting health, safety and security

D2 – Justify recommendations made for minimising the risks, as appropriate, for the setting and service user groups

Introduction

This aim of this assignment is to ensure that you understand the relevance of legislation, policies and procedures that are in place in the health and social care sector to protect workers and service users/patients from harm.

Tasks

1   As a potential professional in the health or social care sector you should understand clearly how legislation controls the delivery of care. Over the years legislation has changed to ensure that the needs of carers and service users are met.

   Describe how the key current legislation related to health, safety and security influences delivery of health and social care. **(P2)**

   Managers and their advisors write policies and procedures based on the key legislation. Using examples from your work experience describe how specific policies and procedures promote health and social care. **(P3)**

2   For this task you can either use your work placement setting or use the setting below:

   You are a worker in a care home and as one of a series of training sessions you have been asked to deliver a presentation that describes the roles and responsibilities of key workers in your placement or a care home.

   You can choose to use flip charts, posters, handouts, PowerPoint, etc to help support your presentation. **(P4)**

The presentation must also explain how the legislation, policies and procedures used in your organisation can promote the health, safety and security of service users, carers and visitors. **(M1)**

Following the presentation write an article that evaluates the effectiveness of those policies and procedures. Include a copy of your presentation (put it onto an A4 sheet if you used large posters) and give examples of how useful and successful the policies and procedures are that have been implemented in the organisation. **(D1)**

3 Select a specific user group that you are familiar with.

Investigate the health and safety of a local environment that the group uses.

You should consider what would be the ideal conditions and then devise a survey that inspects all those issues.

You could choose a park, supermarket, shopping centre, library, community centre, beauty spot, museum, etc. **(P5)**

As a care worker you will be taking the group to that environment. Part of your planning involves a risk assessment of the environment.

Carry out a risk assessment based on the findings of your survey.

Make recommendations that will make risks acceptable. **(M2)**

Give good reasons for the recommendations that you have made to minimise risks. Be clear about the hazards that you have identified; explain whether your recommendations apply to the service user or the setting. **(D2)**

Health, Safety and Security in Health and Social Care

- **Task 2**
- A presentation as part of a training session on roles and responsibilities of key workers in (organisation). You can choose to use flip charts, posters, handouts, PowerPoint etc to help support your presentation. **(P4)**
- The presentation must explain the relevant legislation, state why included and give examples of how implemented in (organisation) **(M1)**

By Elton Johnson.

Roles and Responsibilities of Key People in the Promotion of Health, Safety and Security in St. John's Nursing Home and the Importance of Legislation for Individuals in the Nursing Home.

This is the nursing home where I am doing my placement.

Roles

- Matron – or manager
- Night Sister
- Care workers

Responsibilities

- Matron or Senior Manager – is responsible for the everyday running of the home
  - Policies
  - Accident book
  - Equipment checks
  - Food hygiene
  - Fire drill
  - First Aid

This is a bit extreme, but if staff keep avoiding training sessions this might be what happens to the home!

Promotion of Legislation,

- The Health and Safety at Work etc. Act 1974
- The Health and Safety at Work Regulations 1999
- The Control of Substances Hazardous to Health Regulations 1999

ASSESSOR FEEDBACK FORM

UNIT 3: HEALTH, SAFETY AND SECURITY IN HEALTH AND SOCIAL CARE
ASSIGNMENT – PASS LEVEL ANSWER

Task 2

Elton, you decided to give a PowerPoint presentation to describe the roles and responsibilities of key workers in your placement and to explain how policies, procedures and legislation can promote health, safety and security of service users, carers and visitors.

P4 – Achieved. The presentation was very brief and although no consideration was to be given to the way you presented it, it is a useful experience for the future, so please take it seriously next time.

Try to be familiar with the work so that you do not have to read every single word. Remember that some people get fed up with the 'all singing, all dancing' presentation, keep it simple and stay away from so much animation!

The content was very brief, but you have described the roles and responsibilities of key workers.

M1 – Not awarded. You have included some colourful images, but you have not given enough detail explaining how the legislation is used in your organisation. You have only copied out legislation. To achieve this criterion you should state how your placement has turned legislation into policy and procedure, and discuss how it works in your placement.

D1 – Not attempted.

Health, Safety and Security in Health and Social Care

- A presentation as part of a training session on roles and responsibilities of key workers in (organisation). You can choose to use flip charts, posters, handouts, PowerPoint, etc to help support your presentation. **(P4)**
- The presentation must explain the relevant legislation, state why included and give examples of how implemented in (organisation) **(M1)**

By Tracey Barlow

Roles of staff in Gale's Care Home

- The Manager
- Caretaker
- Care Staff
- Kitchen Staff
- Everyone!

Promotion of Legislation,

- The Health and Safety at Work etc. Act 1974
- The Health and Safety at Work Regulations 1999
- The Control of Substances Hazardous to Health Regulations 1999
- The Food Safety Act 1990
- Manual Handling Regulations 1992
- Reporting of Injuries, Diseases and Dangerous Occurrences Regulations 1995

Responsibilities

- The Manager, Gale Pratt – is responsible for the everyday running of the home
- The caretaker, Jason – is responsible for the maintenance of the home
- The kitchen staff, led by Betty – who is responsible for food and the kitchen

Promotion of legislation etc

- Manual Handling
- Food Safety
- COSHH
- Health and Safety at Work

The End

Any questions?

ASSESSOR FEEDBACK FORM

UNIT 3: HEALTH, SAFETY AND SECURITY IN HEALTH AND SOCIAL CARE
ASSIGNMENT – MERIT LEVEL ANSWER

Task 2

Tracey, you gave a PowerPoint presentation to describe the roles and responsibilities of key workers in your placement and to explain how policies, procedures and legislation can promote health, safety and security of service users, carers and visitors.

P4 – Achieved. The presentation was carefully considered and presented in a confident manner.

You have examined the responsibilities of key workers and described their roles at your workplace.

M1 – Achieved. You have stated how your placement has turned legislation into policy and procedure, and discussed how it works to promote health, safety and security in your placement.

With regard to Manual Handling Regulations you should have included the words "where there is a risk of injury" to ensure your colleagues understood that they are not forbidden to lift even a small, light package!

D1 – Not attempted. You have time to submit the evaluation Tracey and I believe that you will be successful.

To achieve D1 you should evaluate how effective (or not) the policies are that are used in your placement. Ensure that you include an example from each of a selection of policies and procedures.

DISTINCTION LEVEL ANSWER

UNIT 3: HEALTH, SAFETY AND SECURITY IN HEALTH AND SOCIAL CARE
ASSIGNMENT – by Samina Begum
Task 2.

An evaluation of the effectiveness of the policies and procedures in place to promote health, safety and security at my work placement.

My work placement has been carried out at the Health for All Health Centre.

Names of people and places have been changed to meet the requirements of the Data Protection Act 1998.

The sentence above is the first example of how effective policy is and how it promotes security at my placement. As I have changed names, no-one can be identified and no confidential information will be released.

The Health and Safety Executive state that all employers should either display a poster or issue all employees with the following leaflet:

Health and safety law: What you should know

We have a poster in our staff room and all new staff are given a copy of this leaflet.

A policy that covers the requirements of the Manual Handling Act is in place at work, this ensures that all staff are aware of equipment for lifting heavy or awkward items. It demonstrates how people should bend and the muscle groups that they should use to pick up items.

The COSHH Act is implemented at work mainly by the cleaning staff who keep hazardous substances, mainly cleaning liquids, in the correct containers and locked away. We also have a file of safety sheets that state what should be done in the event of spillage, contamination or contact with skin.

Beside the First Aid Box we have a book that meets the RIDDOR requirements. The practice manager checks this following any accidents, incidents or near misses to see if there are further actions that should be carried out or reported to the HSE.

I have attached copies of leaflets that we use at the Health Centre.

Health, Safety and Security in Health and Social Care

- A presentation as part of a training session on roles and responsibilities of key workers in (organisation). You can choose to use flip charts, posters, handouts, PowerPoint, etc to help support your presentation. **(P4)**
- The presentation must explain the relevant legislation, state why included and give examples of how implemented in (organisation) **(M1)**

By Samina Begum.

Roles and Responsibilities of Key Workers in the Promotion of Health, Safety and Security in the Health for All Health Centre

Samina Begum

Roles and Responsibilities

- Practice Manager
- Doctors
- Reception staff
- Cleaners
- All other workers

Responsibilities

- The employer – practice manager
- The doctors
- The reception/secretarial staff

Legislation

- The Health and Safety at Work etc. Act 1974
- The Health and Safety at Work Regulations 1999
- The Control of Substances Hazardous to Health Regulations 1999
- The Food Safety Act 1990
- Manual Handling Operations Regulations 1992
- Reporting of Injuries, Diseases and Dangerous Occurrences Regulations 1995
- Data Protection Act 1998

Promotion of Legislation and Policy

- Risk Assessment
- Manual Handling
- COSHH
- Health and Safety at Work

End

- Useful websites:
- http://www.hse.gov.uk/pubns/indg136.pdf COSHH leaflet
- http://www.hse.gov.uk/pubns/indg275.pdf Health &Safety Management
- http://www.hse.gov.uk/pubns/indg143.pdf ManualHandling Leaflet
- http://www.lmc.org.uk/guidance/dataprotectionact.pdf Data Protection Act updated for GPs

- Any questions?

Insert your company name here

COSHH Summary Form

This form provides details of the hazards and risks associated with the task/substance identified below. You must read the information provided and implement the measures specified on the form.

Assessment Number:	Assessment Date:	Review Date:
Area:	Work Activity:	

Product/substance name(s): Synonyms:	Chemical name: Hazard phrase:

Appearance:

How product is used:

Risks to health:

Factors which increase risks:

Exposure routes: Inhalation ☐   Ingestion ☐   Eye contact ☐   Skin contact ☐
Absorption ☐   Injection ☐

Symptoms of harmful exposure:

Storage precautions:

Transport precautions:

Handling/use precautions:

Personal protective equipment required:

Disposal precautions:

Emergency action
Spillage:
First aid:
Fire:

Emergency action contact:

Additional information
Relevant risk assessment form number:
Medical advice:

Name, address and telephone number of supplier of substance:

ASSESSOR FEEDBACK FORM

UNIT 3: HEALTH, SAFETY AND SECURITY IN HEALTH AND SOCIAL CARE
ASSIGNMENT – DISTINCTION LEVEL ANSWER

Task 2

Samina, your PowerPoint presentation describes the roles and responsibilities of key workers in your placement and explains how policies, procedures and legislation can promote the health, safety and security of service users, carers and visitors.

P4 – Achieved. The presentation was carefully considered and presented in a confident manner.

You have examined the responsibilities of key workers and described their roles at your workplace.

M1 – Achieved. You have stated how your placement has turned legislation into policy and procedure, and discussed how it works to promote health, safety and security in your placement.

D1 – Achieved. You have carried out a good evaluation of the effectiveness of policies implemented in your placement for promoting health, safety and security. Although you have not written pages and pages, what you have written is carefully thought out and meets the assessment criteria. Well done.

Unit 4: Development through the Life Stages

SAMPLE ASSIGNMENT

This assignment meets the following Learning outcomes and Grading criteria:

LO 1 – Understand human growth and development through the life stages

LO 2 – Understand how life factors and events may influence the development of the individual

P1 – Describe physical, intellectual, emotional and social development through the life stages

P2 – Describe the potential influences of five life factors on the development of individuals

P3 – Describe the influences of two predictable and two unpredictable major life events on the development of the individual

M1 – Discuss the nature-nurture debate in relation to individual development

M2 – Explain how major life events can influence the development of the individual

D1 – Evaluate the nature-nurture debate in relation to development of the individual

Introduction

When William Shakespeare wrote about the life stages, he saw seven stages:

'...All the world's a stage,

And all the men and women merely players,

They have their exits and entrances,

And one man in his time plays many parts,

His acts being seven ages. At first the infant,

Mewling and puking in the nurse's arms.

Then, the whining schoolboy with his satchel

And shining morning face, creeping like a snail

Unwillingly to school. ...'

Tasks

1 As a professional in the health and social care sector you will need to understand the needs of individuals at all the different stages of their life, (as described by Shakespeare), but starting before infancy, to death at old age.

Investigate physical, intellectual, emotional and social development needs throughout life; document your findings as a report or table that can be referred to when checking facts at particular life stages.

You should include eight stages:

Conception

Pregnancy

Birth and infancy, 0–3 years

Childhood, 4–9 years

Adolescence, 10–18 years

Adulthood, 19–65 years

Older adulthood, 65+ years

The final stages of life

Note. This is not an anatomy and physiology unit so does not require great anatomical detail when investigating the physical aspects of development. **(P1)**

2 Life is influenced by many factors. Select one factor from each of the following groups – genetic, biological, environmental, socio-economic, lifestyle.

Describe in detail how your chosen factors could influence the development of an individual. **(P2)**

Factors that influence life can have a large or small impact, and can be predictable or unpredictable.

Describe the influences of two predictable and two unpredictable major life events on the development of the individual. **(P3)**

Write a case study (or a story) that clearly demonstrates how major life events can influence the development of an individual.

You could select the life of a television soap character, or invent a character to meet your requirements.

Include, where relevant, psychological theory. **(M2)**

3 Using the case study (or story) that you used in Task 2, discuss how far the behaviours, ideas, and feelings of the character are innate (nature), and how far are they all learned (nurture)? **(M1)**

Using the previous character from your case study (or story), evaluate the nature–nurture debate. Use examples from the case study supported by theory to maintain your evaluation. **(D1)**

PASS LEVEL ANSWER

UNIT 4: DEVELOPMENT THROUGH THE LIFE STAGES
ASSIGNMENT – by Shelly Sturgess
Task 1.

Development Needs	Physical	Intellectual	Emotional	Social
Stages				
Conception	Development taking place in the reproductive system	0000	0000	0000
Pregnancy	Development taking place in the uterus Baby develops over 40 weeks to aprox 7–8lbs	0000	0000	0000
0–3	Born with physical reflexes Lift head by 3 months Sit 6–8 months Crawl 6–10 months Upright 10–12 months Walk 10–16 months Kick & throw ball 18–24 months Pedal trike 2–3 years.	Language becomes clear 6–9 months. 2–word sentences Ability to see other's perspective 3 & 4 word sentences Understands false belief	Attached to mother, then all immediate family. Friends when starts play school/nursery	Will not share. Fears strangers 10–14 months Plays with peers 16 months Self aware 18+ months Turn taking Same sex peer choice
4–9	Climbs stairs one foot at a time Kicks and throws large ball Hops & skips Jumps rope. Skips. May ride bike. Continued gross & fine motor skills Puberty starts for some girls	Continued language development Various skills developing. Memory strategies Concrete operations skills	Gender stability	Beginning individual friendships Aggression and more verbal Negotiation, rather than defiance

Development Needs	Physical	Intellectual	Emotional	Social
Stages				
10–18	Puberty starts for some boys Girls' height spurt Average age of menarche 13 Boys height spurt Major pubertal change begins for boys Puberty completed for girls 16	Formal operations develop Systematic analysis Some deductive logic	Parent–child conflict peaks at beginning of puberty Maximum impact of peer group pressure Normal time for first dating	Self–esteem declines Self–esteem begins to rise and continues to rise for remainder of adolescence
19–65	Puberty completed for boys 18–19 Peak function on virtually all measures 20–27 Best time for childbearing 20–27 Athletic performance at its peak in most sports Many types of physical changes 40–50 Vision changes; decline in aerobic capacity; skin changes; slowing of nervous system and reaction time Menopause in women around 50, increased bone loss, increased loss of muscle tissue	Increasing IQ. Improving performance on intelligence tests IQ increases to about 50–55, then gradual decline Little change in memory till 60–65	Typical time for acquisition of spouse, parent, worker roles. Highest levels of depression and loneliness in one's 20s Mellowing after peak of individuality, assertiveness, and confidence at 40–45	Searching for partner Finding partner and marriage Increasing self–confidence, assertiveness, independence, greater individualization Decline in marital satisfaction after birth of first child and throughout rest of young adulthood
65+	Increased rate of hearing loss Significant decline in hearing, speed of response; continued gradual decline on most physical measures;	Gradual decline on all cognitive measures.	Social involvement related to life satisfaction.	High rate of social involvement. Retirement for most working adults

141

Development Needs	Physical	Intellectual	Emotional	Social
Stages				
Final stages	Incidence of disease and disability increased	Decline on cognitive measures, wide individual variability.	Rise in incidence of depression past age 75	Decline in social involvement for those whose physical disabilities make mobility problematic

ASSESSOR FEEDBACK FORM

UNIT 4: DEVELOPMENT THROUGH THE LIFE STAGES
ASSIGNMENT – PASS LEVEL ANSWER

P1 – You have achieved this criterion Shelly. You decided to document your information as a table, this is clear and concise.

The table has identified the important factors to be considered at each stage. Obviously there is much more that could be included – the task does not ask for inclusion of theorists, but this would be a good place to start identifying their work, eg mention of Ainsworth in the social column with 'fear of strangers', etc.

You have made a good start and have earned the Pass criterion.

UNIT 4: DEVELOPMENT THROUGH THE LIFE STAGES
ASSIGNMENT – by Julie Wright
Task 2.

P2 – FACTORS THAT INFLUENCE THE DEVELOPMENT OF AN INDIVIDUAL:

Genetic – Down Syndrome

People with Down Syndrome are people rather than Down sufferers. They have strengths and weaknesses; they have many of the same needs as other people in addition to some extra needs.

The influence of Down syndrome on the individual depends very much on the quality of health care, education and community support provided as they progress through life. Like all children, progress for children with Down syndrome is influenced by family life and parents' child rearing skills, inclusion with peers at home and in preschool, and the quality of education available. It is also influenced by biological make–up, and some children with Down syndrome are born with more biological disadvantages than others. The most powerful influence on the progress of a baby with Down syndrome is to be loved, wanted and absorbed into the everyday life of the family and of the community.

The development of a baby born with Down syndrome will vary according to the help and support given as well as on the severity of the disorder. There might be strengths in social understanding, self–help skills and behaviour, and weaknesses in motor development and speech and language skills. Speech and language skills will depend on hearing ability which is often affected.

Visual processing and visual memory skills are usually strengths and can be used to support children's learning. By 5 years of age, many children with Down syndrome can achieve some of the same developmental targets as their peers. Most will be walking, toilet trained and able to feed themselves and dress with minimal help. Most will be able to fit into the expectations of the mainstream classroom, regulate their own behaviour and behave in a socially acceptable way.

Most children will have significantly delayed spoken language. They will understand more than they can say, and their spoken language will not be clear. Many will have some of the basic concepts and knowledge for learning number, maths and reading.

In the 5–11 year period many children with Down syndrome will have the same goals as their peers although they might not achieve quite the same levels.

The 11–16 period is significant for all teens. It is considered by some that the physical, social and emotional needs of teenagers with Down syndrome are essentially the same as those of other teenagers. These young people should be supported and encouraged in their development, they might also still be developing language, speech and numeracy skills.

Biological – Rubella in pregnancy

If a mother develops rubella (German Measles) during the very early stages of pregnancy there is a strong chance that child might be born with congenital rubella, the virus can remain in the blood stream for up to 20 months following birth, although the child will not be contagious. All children affected by Rubella have the capacity to learn and achieve, but without the right kind of help, their mental and physical development may be slower because of lack of stimulation. Early intervention, with continuing intensive educational support is the key to a child's future development, although extra support may be needed throughout a person's lifetime. The potential influence of rubella on the development of the individual depends on the stage of pregnancy that infection occurs. Rubella in the first two months of pregnancy is likely to affect the baby and may cause a number of impairments. After 18 weeks gestation, although rubella infection may be passed on to the baby, the chances of the baby being affected may be minimal. The most commonly affected organs include the ears, the eyes, and the heart.

Between three and seven weeks the eye lenses may be affected and become cloudy, cataracts may develop.

Heart defects are common if rubella is contracted very early in pregnancy. They can be severe and the woman would probably receive counselling and be offered termination.

A common problem for babies affected by the rubella virus is hearing loss. This can vary considerably from mild to severe, and may affect one or both ears. This part of the ear damaged is the inner ear or Cochlea which links the ear to the brain. The hearing loss is known as sensori neural. The amount of hearing loss can vary a great deal, and hearing may deteriorate over a period of time.

The rubella virus may or may not affect the child's brain, and difficulties can vary from mild to severe.

Children who have been affected by Rubella may have to cope with an impairment of both sight and hearing, as well as other disabilities – although this will vary a great deal. Many children will have some sight and/or hearing however, and it is important to make as much use of these possible. The other senses – touch and smell in particular – must also be developed to the full.

The biggest challenges facing children affected by Rubella will be to learn to communicate, to move around safely, and to find out about the world around them. These children must get specialist help which is geared towards their particular combination of abilities and impairments as soon as possible. Intensive one–to–one teaching developed for work with deaf and blind children for example, can help them to understand the human interaction that is the basis of communication. Children can learn various ways to communicate such as using symbols, objects of reference, sign language, and Braille.

Environmental – Employment

In Western society having a job is important for wellbeing. Without income from work the individual might develop anxieties about every day life and living, for example, money for food, money for shelter and warmth – the basic necessities of life.

The influence of lack of work can impact on the development of the entire family. If the main wage earner is out of work all will feel the effects, holidays, hobbies and social life are likely to be curtailed. Life–style is usually dependent on income; a meal in a five star restaurant or the burger bar; private or state schooling; private or state health care; holidays in far–flung places or a day trip to the nearest coastal resort. The social development of the individual is obviously suffering from lack of employment.

Physical development might also be affected. As the nutritional status of the individual deteriorates then there is the opportunity for debilitating disease and infection to take hold. This is compounded if money is not available for heating and shelter.

Unemployment can lead to break up of couples and of families. The emotional effect on the individuals involved can be disastrous. Unemployment is considered to be a major source of mental stress and loss of self–esteem which in turn may lead to depression. From the psychological point of view being fired or made redundant from work, and change in financial state all rate in the top twenty stressors of the Holmes and Rahe Scale.

Homelessness has resulted from unemployment in the past and doubtless will happen again. The sight of young people (and not so young) sleeping rough in cardboard boxes or in shop doorways might be less common than a few years ago, but that is usually because the police have been moving people on, not because of a drop in homelessness.

Many homeless people have alcohol–related problems, many are in need of medical attention, and many have mental health problems.

Having become unemployed lessens the chance of gaining further employment. Access to work and the financial rewards diminishes unless opportunity to re-train or move to an area of high employment presents.

Socio-economic – Media

It might at first not appear obvious how 'media' can influence the development of the individual.

The term 'Media' includes the various means of mass communication; television, internet, radio, magazines, and newspapers, and all those people involved in their production.

There has been much research over the years investigating the influence of television on the development of children. Television has been linked to the development of aggression and violence, and to crime and mass murders.

In addition to violence, the media has been accused of stereotyping aspects of life which can lead to undesirable prejudices and so influence development of not only the watcher/reader, but also the individual being stereotyped. Children's programmes often exaggerate stereotypes (goodies and baddies), and children often have their only contact with some minority groups through television.

Not everyone responds to stereotypes in the same manner and it is difficult to separate our inherent attitudes from what we learn from the media.

In addition to the stereotyping influences of the media, there is the ethical issue of ownership and control of the media. If 'media' has the power to influence development of the individual, control of media is an issue of concern, whether the controller is rich, ruling class, unions or televangelist!

Lifestyle – Nutrition

Much has been written regarding the influence of diet on development, including malnutrition, types of diet, eating habits, pharmacological effects, food allergy, fatty acid deficiency and possibly food additives. The image of 'the perfect body' influences the way many people eat, the perfect body image can vary according to fashion, sport and culture.

The range of developmental behaviour thought to be affected by nutrition is wide and includes attention conduct disorder and mood. Recent and ongoing research has linked hyperactivity with nutrition and diet. For children showing behaviour problems such as hyperactivity the use of dietary manipulation tends to be a more acceptable approach to treatment than the use of drugs. A study is currently underway to investigate the

147

possible effects of additives on behaviour in the general population of children.

P3 – THE INFLUENCES OF TWO PREDICTABLE AND TWO UNPREDICTABLE MAJOR LIFE EVENTS ON THE DEVELOPMENT OF THE INDIVIDUAL.

PREDICTABLE:

Marriage

Marriage is seen by psychologists as being linked to health and happiness. This is probably not surprising, a single person living alone is less likely to look after their nutritional status and well being, than a couple who tend to look after each other and support physical development, whether it is through exercising together or relaxing as well as looking after each other's health and well being.

The successful marriage can enhance the development of each individual's psychological well being through positive interactions – just being 'nice' to each other. It is when the negative interactions outweigh the positive that separation and divorce become likely.

Death

Death sometimes comes as a shock to family and friends – when it is early or sudden. However, death is inevitable, it is an absolute certainty. It is the remaining partner or the family that experience the consequences of death and whose development is influenced.

In Western society death is often a taboo subject and is avoided as a topic of conversation, other societies deal differently with dying and the death itself is celebrated.

Elizabeth Kubler–Ross (1969) introduced stages of grief which many relatives and friends will go through. There is no specific progression or timing for the stages, but should an individual become 'stuck' in a particular stage it can have a marked impact on development.

UNPREDICTABLE:

Divorce

Divorce is increasingly common in Western society; however the number of divorces in England and Wales fell by 8 per cent in 2005 to 141,750, compared with 153,399 in 2004. This is the second consecutive year that divorces have fallen and is the lowest number since 2000 (National Statistics August 2006)*.

Even though the divorce rate is high it is still an unexpected and often shocking occurrence. Divorce rates as the second highest stressor on the Holmes and Rahe Scale.

Research has found that the effect on development of the individual is in same cases similar to death, not only for the individual but often for the affected family, in that it involves sorrow, grief and anger.

Divorce has been found to cause psychiatric problems in children, although some research has found that a happy single parent family is better than a disturbed family home.

* National Statistics http://www.statistics.gov.uk/pdfdir/div0806.pdf [accessed 01/05/2007]

Abuse

Abuse can occur during any stage of lifespan development; child, adult, elders. Abuse is something can be done to others – and to the self. At whatever stage and to whomever it occurs it is always unpredictable. Surely in this 'civilised' society we would not allow abuse to occur, if we could predict it, we would stop it – wouldn't we?

Horror stories of abuse – whether child, elder or domestic, that reaches the media and awareness of the general public are fortunately few and far between, however abuse is occurring every day in some area of the country.

The influence on the development of the individual is enormous and covers all aspects of psychological, intellectual, emotional and social development and is invariably damaging.

It is the life–stage, abuse type, and personality type that will dictate how the abuse will influence development of the individual. At its most extreme abuse will lead to death.

M2 – A CASE STUDY THAT CLEARLY DEMONSTRATES HOW MAJOR LIFE EVENTS CAN INFLUENCE THE DEVELOPMENT OF AN INDIVIDUAL

Stacey was thirteen when she ran away from home. She ran following yet another beating from her step father. The abuse had been happening regularly since she was eight. Stacey's mother married Kev, who did not have a job, soon after her husband died. Stacey missed her dad who had died of cancer when she was seven, and when she shouted at Kev 'you're not my dad' he beat her. After the first time it became a regular occurrence. As the beatings got more frequent Stacey started to lose her confidence and when she changed school her work deteriorated. She become unruly and violent at school and when mum and Kev were called to see the teachers, she got another beating. Stacey decided to run away soon after her sister was born – it was quite a shock, to find that her mother no longer cared for her and was happy to spend all her time with the baby and to let Kev discipline Stacey in his own way.

When Stacey left home she was malnourished as she had lost her appetite soon after the beatings started, she only ate because she needed to and did not enjoy her food at all.

Stacey's development had been influenced by major life events; death, bereavement, marriage, abuse, stepfather, changing school, birth of a sibling, leaving home, to the point where she could no longer deal with the stressors forced on her. All aspects of her life had been affected – psychological, intellectual, emotional and social.

For Stacey to return to a positive and happy life would take an enormous amount of help.

It can be seen that Stacey's development through life has been affected by both nature – her inherited health and personality, and by nurture, the socialisation and environment that have affected Stacey's upbringing.

Erikson said that between the ages of 13–18 the young person should adapt to the changes that come with puberty and should search for new values. The people in Stacey's life who should have been good role models – her parents, have not been a positive factor on her development. Stacey would have a very confused view of life, making it difficult for her to make choices about her future.

ASSESSOR FEEDBACK FORM

UNIT 4: DEVELOPMENT THROUGH THE LIFE STAGES
ASSIGNMENT – MERIT LEVEL ANSWER

P2 – criterion achieved. You have tackled this task well, Julie. You have selected five life factors and described their potential influences on the development of the individual. Your discussion on Down Syndrome is well researched and informative.

P3 – criterion not yet achieved. You have made an interesting choice of predictable (marriage and death) and unpredictable (divorce and abuse) influences on the development of the individual.

Your discussion is rather brief; you should have included far more depth and given examples from your work placement that would support your statements, eg you might have talked about Mrs Smith, whose husband died last year. How is she dealing with her bereavement? How has the bereavement affected her relationship with her carers? With the other residents in the home? Is she behaving 'normally'? Does she go out? Has her appetite been affected? Etc.

M2 – criterion achieved. This is a fascinating case study Julie, you have described several major life events and how they have affected her development. You have introduced some psychological theory and related it appropriately to the case study. Well done.

I am very pleased to see that you have started to reference your work. You should also include a bibliography at the end of the work – a list of the books that you have used to help write your assignment. Although this is not a requirement of the grading criteria we have discussed its importance during lessons. Including a bibliography will enable assessors to identify your sources and follow up your work. You should keep notes of the sources you use (books, videos, Internet URLs, etc). If you copy work, you must include the name of the author, the page number and the date of publication. This will avoid accusations of plagiarism – cheating, by using another person's thoughts or writing them down as if they are your own.

DISTINCTION LEVEL ANSWER

**UNIT 4: DEVELOPMENT THROUGH THE LIFE STAGES
ASSIGNMENT – by Tracey Barlow**

**A CASE STUDY THAT CLEARLY DEMONSTRATES HOW MAJOR
LIFE EVENTS CAN INFLUENCE THE DEVELOPMENT OF AN
INDIVIDUAL
Task 3.**

M1 – The Case Study.

Stacey was thirteen when she ran away from home. She ran following yet another beating from her step father. The abuse had been happening regularly since she was eight. At first when her mother married Kev they had all been happy, but that had soon changed. Stacey missed her dad who had died of cancer when she was seven, and when she shouted at Kev 'you're not my dad' he beat her. After the first time it became a regular occurrence. As the beatings got more frequent Stacey started to lose her confidence and when she changed school her work deteriorated. She become unruly and violent at school and when mum and Kev were called to see the teachers, she got another beating. Stacey decided to run away soon after her sister was born – it was quite a shock, to find that her mother no longer cared for her and was happy to spend all her time with the baby and to let Kev discipline Stacey in his own way.

When Stacey left home she was malnourished as she had lost her appetite soon after the beatings started, she only ate because she needed to and did not enjoy her food at all.

Stacey's development had been influenced by major life events; death, bereavement, marriage, abuse, stepfather, changing school, birth of a sibling, leaving home, to the point where she could no longer deal with the stressors forced on her. All aspects of her life had been affected – psychological, intellectual, emotional and social.

For Stacey to return to a positive and happy life would take an enormous amount of help.

D1 – The Nature-Nurture Debate, a Discussion and Evaluation.

Stacey's development had been a happy balance of nature and nurture until she reached the age of eight. Even when dealing with the death of her father, although tragic, Stacey had gained comfort from her strong character – a mix of both her parents, and from the encouragement she received from her mother.

Stacey had been a happy little girl, her upbringing influencing gender development by the toys and dolls that she was given to play with and the pretty dresses that she wore. Bio-psychologists say that gender is innate and is a direct result of genetic and hormonal influences, however learning theory argues that gender is socially constructed and reinforced.

By losing confidence and running away from home it would appear that Stacey's development is not progressing normally, the stressors that she has experienced have put enormous pressure on her. The Behaviourists would say that the environment has played a role in the development of stress – the bio-psychologists would say Stacey's stress is genetic and neurochemicals are responsible for her mental development.

Stacey's aggression and violence at school would be said by the Behaviourists to be learnt from her father, through observation and imitation. The Bio-psychologists believe that aggression is innate and is influenced by hormones acting on areas of the brain.

It could also be said that the stress suffered by Stacey's step father as he was unemployed increased the likelihood of poor parenting and so lead to antisocial behaviour of the child, Stacey, who ran away.

Francis Horrowitz (1987), an Interactionist who look at a combination of nature and nurture, would say that Stacey suffered from being a vulnerable child in a poor environment, and this led to her poor outcomes.

ASSESSOR FEEDBACK FORM

UNIT 4: DEVELOPMENT THROUGH THE LIFE STAGES
ASSIGNMENT – DISTINCTION LEVEL ANSWER

M1 – criterion not yet achieved. Tracey, this is a very brief discussion. Having identified the possible reasons for Stacey's impaired development, you now need to enlarge on this by relating it to the nature-nurture debate, and considering the work of specific theorists. For example, what sort of internal models had Stacey developed by this stage? Would the discipline techniques used by her parents have any bearing on her development? (John Bowlby; Gerald Patterson, etc.) You do not need to discuss 'how' or 'why' for this task; just consider the theories that might be relevant.

D1 – criterion achieved. You have evaluated the nature-nurture debate in relation to Stacey's development, supporting your discussion with theory from nature-nurture and from the Interactionists. Well done Tracy.

Tracey, you need to complete the work to achieve M1. This should not be difficult as you have understood the theories and used them in D1.

Unit 5: Fundamentals of Anatomy and Physiology for Health and Social Care

SAMPLE ASSIGNMENT

This assignment meets the following Learning outcomes and Grading criteria:

LO 2 – Understand the functioning of the body systems associated with energy metabolism

LO 3 – Understand how homeostatic mechanisms operate in the maintenance of an internal environment

P4 – Describe the role of energy in the body and the physiology of three named body systems in relation to energy metabolism

P5 – Describe the concept of homeostasis and the homeostatic mechanisms that regulate heart rate, breathing rate, body temperature and blood glucose levels

M1 – Explain the physiology of three named body systems in relation to energy metabolism

M2 – Explain the probable homeostatic responses to changes in the internal environment during exercise

D1 – Use examples to explain how body systems interrelate with each other

D2 – Explain the importance of homeostasis in maintaining the healthy functioning of the body

Introduction

This assignment will enable you to demonstrate the knowledge and understanding that you have gained to describe and explain the role of energy in named body systems; and to describe and explain homeostasis in the healthy human body.

Task

1 Energy is the ability to do work, and as you have been discovering, the body is working all the time, even when you are asleep.

Describe the role of energy in the human body.

Describe the functioning of three systems of the body and relate them to energy metabolism. **(P4)**

Using the same three body systems that you have described, give examples of their working in relation to energy metabolism. **(M1)**

In order for the body to function effectively it is necessary for the different body systems to work together. Using examples, explain how this happens. **(D1)**

2 In order for the human body to function efficiently it must maintain a constant internal environment. Describe your understanding of homeostasis and the homeostatic mechanisms that regulate the following:

- Heart rate
- Breathing rate
- Body temperature
- Blood glucose levels **(P5)**

Even if you do not take regular exercise you will be aware of changes that occur in your body if you do anything strenuous. Even just running for the bus might make you gasp for breath, your heart start to race and your body start to sweat! Explain the probable homeostatic responses to changes in the internal environment during exercise. **(M2)**

Having said that the body **must** maintain a constant internal environment in order to function in a healthy manner, now give details **why** homeostasis is so important for the body. **(D2)**

PASS, MERIT AND DISTINCTION LEVEL ANSWERS

By Mo Azir
ENERGY METABOLISM
Task 1.
PASS ANSWER – DESCRIBE

The role of energy in the body

The body requires energy for all functions, movement, reproduction, respiration etc.

The energy is obtained mainly from food and must be changed into a form that the cells can use i.e. molecules of adenosine triphospate (ATP). Chemical energy is stored as ATP and heat

In the human body the following types of energy are utilised: electrical, electro-magnetic, chemical, heat.

The human body derives energy from food – measured in units of kilocalories (Kcal) (or Calories, C).

One Calorie is the amount of energy required to raise the temperature of 1kg of water 1°C.

The energy is used by the body in three different ways:
- Basal metabolism – the energy required to keep the body functioning at minimal level
- Physical activity
- Thermogenesis – or assimilation of food

The three factors add together to make up the metabolic rate. .If the caloric intake exceeds the needs for metabolism, there will be weight gain.

The physiology of three systems of the body related to energy metabolism:

The gross anatomy and physiology is not considered here as it is discussed in other tasks.

The physiology of the Respiratory system in relation to energy metabolism

Oxygen is required by the cells as it contributes to the production of ATP that is necessary for energy metabolism. Oxygen is removed from the air breathed in and an interchange of gases takes place between the blood and the air in the alveoli.

Gas exchange between air and blood occurs at the alveoli. The surface area of the alveoli is about 70–100m^2, this gives a large area in which exchange can take place.

On inspiration air enters the lungs and passes to the alveoli. Oxygen diffuses through the aveoli walls and into the blood where it combines with haemoglobin in the red blood cells.

Carbon dioxide diffuses out of the blood into the alveoli, it is then breathed out.

The physiology of the Digestive system in relation to energy metabolism
Glucose is the preferred fuel for production of ATP. Glucose is obtained from the digestion of carbohydrate, it is absorbed into the capillaries of the villi of the small intestine, transported by the portal circulation to the liver.

In the liver glucose may be oxidised to provide chemical energy in the form of ATP.

The oxidation of carbohydrate and fat provides most of the energy required by the body, when glycogen stores are low the body can make glucose from non-carbohydrates sources e.g. amino acids, glycerol.

The physiology of the Muscular system in relation to energy metabolism
When a muscle contracts it uses energy.

The energy is derived mainly from glucose (stored as glycogen). Glucose and oxygen are carried in the blood

Muscle fibres can be grouped according to what kind of tissue they are found in; skeletal muscle, smooth muscle, and cardiac muscle. The primary function of skeletal muscles is contraction.

Before a muscle fibre can contract it has to receive an impulse from a nerve cell.

Nerve cells regulate the function of skeletal muscle fibres by controlling the frequency of action potentials produced in the muscle cell membrane.

MERIT ANSWER – EXPLAIN
The physiology of three systems of the body related to energy metabolism:
Muscular; Respiratory; Digestive

The physiology of the Respiratory system in relation to energy metabolism
The respiratory system enables the production of energy by supplying the cells with a continuous supply of oxygen. It is also responsible for eliminating carbon dioxide, a by-product of cell metabolism. Cell (or tissue) respiration is the process that releases the energy in organic molecules such as glucose. The gross anatomical structures of the respiratory system provide the mechanism for transporting oxygen.

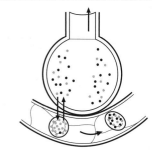

The physiology of the Muscular system in relation to energy metabolism
Muscle fibres are covered by a plasma membrane sheath – sarcolemma.

Tube like extensions from the sarcolemma pass through the muscle fibre from one side to the other through the diameter of the fibre, these are called transverse tubules.

The nuclei of muscle fibres ("muscle cells") are located at the edges of the diameter of the fibre, adjacent to the sarcolemma. A single muscle fibre may have many nuclei.

157

The cytoplasm present in muscle cells is called sarcoplasm

Sarcoplasm contains many mitochondria – the energy producing units. These produce ATP.

The sarcoplasmic reticulum is a network of membrane-enclosed tubules similar to smooth endoplasmic reticulum. This is present in muscle cells and extends throughout the sarcoplasm of the cell. The function of sarcoplasmic reticulum is to store calcium ions, which are necessary for muscle contraction.

Myoglobin is also present in the sarcoplasm of muscle cells. This red pigment gives skeletal muscles their colour and stores oxygen until it is required by the mitochondria for the production of ATP.

The skeletal muscle action potentials trigger a series of chemical events in the muscle fibers that results in the mechanical process of muscle contraction

The immediate source of energy for this muscle contraction is adenosine triphospate (ATP). Muscle contraction requires (ATP) and blood vessels deliver the nutrients and oxygen to produce it.

- ATP supplies in muscles provide enough energy only for the first few seconds of exercise
- Anaerobic respiration can supply energy only for up to two minutes of high intensity exercise
- Aerobic respiration can supply energy indefinitely for low intensity activity

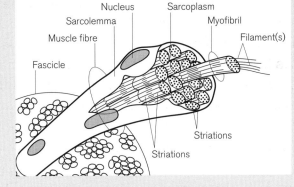

The physiology of the **Digestive** system in relation to energy metabolism

Glucose is actively transported into the cells of the small intestine and across the walls of the capillaries.

Active transport is necessary as diffusion would be too slow to meet the body's needs.

Glucose is broken down in the body to give energy, carbon dioxide and water. Catabolism of glucose occurs – the breaking down of large molecules into smaller ones, releasing chemical energy which is stored as ATP.

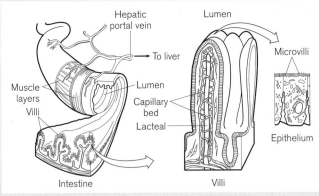

DISTINCTION ANSWER
Explain how the body systems interrelate with each other

The body systems work together in several ways, for example, if a person is exercising their somatic nervous system will tell the skeletal muscles to start working. The working muscles will demand energy. The energy will be produced by ATP in the cells. The cardiovascular system will have delivered oxygen and glucose to the cells where ATP is produced.

Glucose will come from the digestive system, oxygen from the respiratory system.

As the individual works harder the skeletal muscles produce large amounts of energy in the form of heat – the skin will redden and sweat will be produced as the capillaries dilate. The hypothalamus in the brain (part of the endocrine system) regulates body temperature through stimulating the sweat glands by autonomic nerve stimulation. The breathing rate will increase to meet the demand from the muscles for more oxygen. The breathing rate is instructed to increase by the autonomic nervous system.

The respiratory system supplies oxygen to, and removes waste carbon dioxide from, the other systems of the body.

The digestive system supplies nutrients (in the form of glucose) via the blood stream, to the cells where it is required.

The musculoskeletal system uses energy in the form of ATP to contract and relax muscles for specific roles i.e. skeletal muscles use energy for

The nervous system interrelate with the preceding three systems as follows; the autonomic nervous system (ANS) adjusts breathing and heart rates as required by the demands of other systems of the body e.g. for exercise; for heat control. The ANS also keeps digestion going.

The somatic nervous system deals with sensation perception and cognitive processes – it also sends impulses to move muscles for voluntary actions.

The cardiovascular system has many functions that interrelate; it transports gases, oxygen to the lungs and tissues, and carbon dioxide from the tissues to the lungs; transports nutrients, including glucose, from the intestine to tissues; the cardiovascular system transports hormones from endocrine glands where they are produced, to other organs where they influence cellular activity.

ASSESSOR FEEDBACK FORM

FUNDAMENTALS OF ANATOMY AND PHYSIOLOGY FOR HEALTH AND SOCIAL CARE

Task 1

P4 – criterion achieved. You have tackled this task well Mo, describing the role of energy in the human body and the physiology of the Muscular, Respiratory, and Digestive systems in relation to energy metabolism.

M1 – criterion achieved. A well explained answer Mo. You have selected relevant and colourful illustrations; I would like to see these referenced please.

D1 – criterion achieved. This is a brief answer but by giving the example of exercise you have addressed